REVISE GCSE
French
PRACTICE PAPERS

THE REVISE SERIES
Available in print or online

Online editions for all titles in the Revise series are available from Spring 2014.

Presented on our ActiveLearn platform, you can view the full book and customise it by adding notes, comments and weblinks.

Print edition

Revise GCSE French Practice Papers   9781292013725

Online edition

Revise GCSE French Practice Papers   9781292013732

Audio files
Audio files for the listening exercises in this book can be found at: www.pearsonschools.co.uk/mflrevisionaudio

These Practice Papers are designed to complement your classroom and home learning, and to help prepare you for the exam. They are designed to work in combination with the Revise GCSE French Revision Guide and Workbook for AQA and Edexcel and Pearson's main GCSE French 2009 series.

For the full range of Pearson revision titles across GCSE, BTEC and AS Level visit:
www.pearsonschools.co.uk/revise

ALWAYS LEARNING

PEARSON

Contents

Audio files

Audio files for the listening exercises in this book can be found at: www.pearsonschools.co.uk/mflrevisionaudio

1   Read the following signs in a French town.

Write the correct letter in each box.

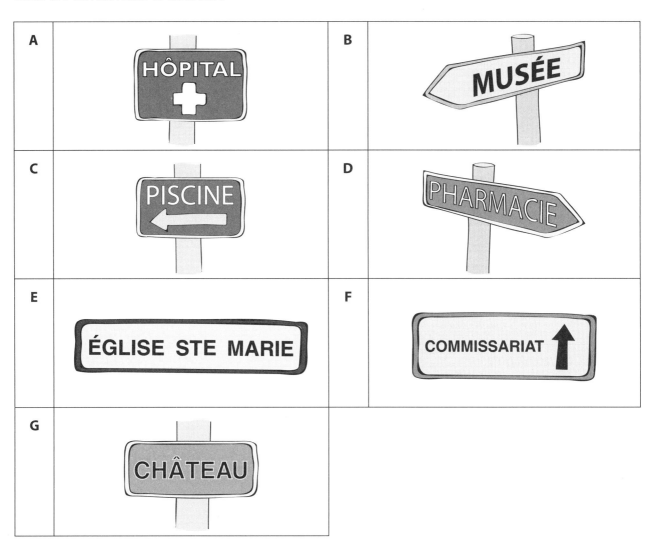

A	HÔPITAL	**B**	MUSÉE
C	PISCINE	**D**	PHARMACIE
E	ÉGLISE STE MARIE	**F**	COMMISSARIAT
G	CHÂTEAU		

Example: You want to get some painkillers.   `D`

1   **(a)**   You want to visit a castle.   ☐   *(1 mark)*

1   **(b)**   You would like to go swimming.   ☐   *(1 mark)*

1   **(c)**   You are looking for a church.   ☐   *(1 mark)*

1   **(d)**   You want to report a theft.   ☐   *(1 mark)*

2   Read the following comments about hobbies.

A	J'adore faire du vélo.
B	Je regarde souvent la télé.
C	La natation m'intéresse beaucoup.
D	La lecture, c'est génial.
E	Ma passion, c'est jouer aux échecs.
F	J'aime bien faire les magasins.
G	J'aime beaucoup jouer sur mon ordinateur.

Which hobby is mentioned?

Write the correct letter in each box.

Example: Watching TV   B

2   **(a)**   Reading   ☐   *(1 mark)*

2   **(b)**   Chess   ☐   *(1 mark)*

2   **(c)**   Cycling   ☐   *(1 mark)*

2   **(d)**   Shopping   ☐   *(1 mark)*

3

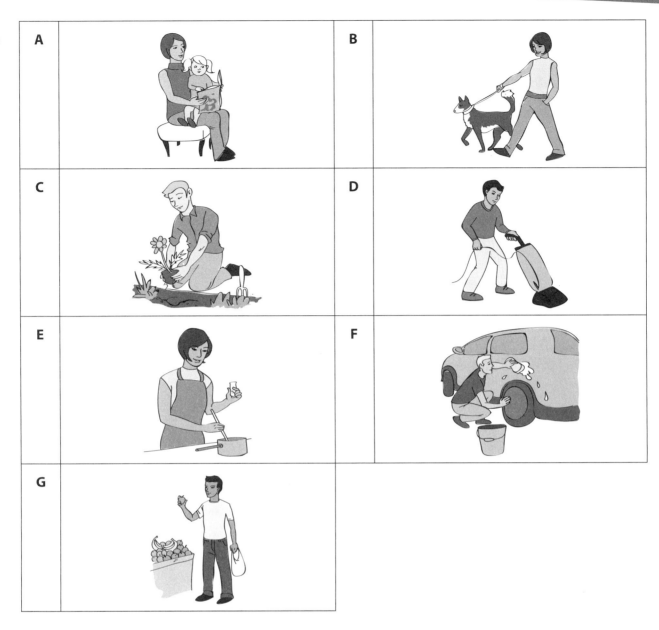

A	B
C	D
E	F
G	

How do the following young people earn pocket money?

Write the correct letter in each box.

Example: Je fais du babysitting pour ma tante.   A

3   **(a)**   Je travaille dans le jardin.   ☐   *(1 mark)*

3   **(b)**   Moi, je dois promener le chien.   ☐   *(1 mark)*

3   **(c)**   Je prépare le repas du soir tous les jours.   ☐   *(1 mark)*

3   **(d)**   Le samedi, je lave la voiture de ma mère.   ☐   *(1 mark)*

4   Read these young people's views on holidays.

Léa: Moi, j'aime bien passer mes vacances au bord de la mer car je trouve ça relaxant. L'année dernière, je suis allée en Espagne avec quelques copines et nous avons fait de la planche à voile pour la première fois. C'était difficile mais marrant. L'année prochaine, je vais aller en Angleterre parce que je voudrais perfectionner mon anglais.

Mylène: Je pars souvent en vacances avec ma famille mais nous ne logeons jamais dans un hôtel car c'est très cher. Nous faisons toujours du camping et j'aime ça. Nous venons de rentrer de nos vacances en Allemagne où nous nous sommes vraiment bien amusés.

Chloé: Normalement, je passe mes vacances dans le sud de la France, chez mon grand-père. Il habite dans une grande ferme. Il y a un terrain de camping bien équipé en face d'une école mais je loge chez lui à la ferme. L'année prochaine, j'irai en Allemagne avec un groupe scolaire et j'espère qu'il fera beau. Nous logerons dans un petit hôtel au centre-ville.

Answer the following questions.

Write **L** (Léa), **M** (Mylène) or **C** (Chloé) in each box.

Example:	Who likes going to the seaside?	L	
4 **(a)**	Who has just returned from holidays in Germany?		*(1 mark)*
4 **(b)**	Who never stays in a hotel on holiday?		*(1 mark)*
4 **(c)**	Who is going on a school trip next year?		*(1 mark)*
4 **(d)**	Who tried a new sport last year?		*(1 mark)*
4 **(e)**	Who is hoping to improve her language skills by going on holiday?		*(1 mark)*

5   Read this description of Marc's school.

> Mon collège est assez grand et il y a mille cinq cents élèves et plus de cent cinquante profs. Ma matière préférée, c'est le dessin et je m'entends très bien avec mon professeur. Par contre, je n'aime pas l'espagnol car je trouve ça barbant et inutile. Les cours commencent à huit heures et demie et je dois me lever tôt parce que je vais au collège en car. Je déteste ça. Le règlement n'est pas strict et j'ai plein de copains, alors ça va en général.

Answer the following questions **in English**.

Example: How many pupils go to Marc's school? .....1500.....

5   **(a)**   What is his favourite subject?

....

(1 mark)

5   **(b)**   Why does he dislike Spanish? Give **two** reasons.

....

....

(2 marks)

5   **(c)**   When do his lessons start?

....

(1 mark)

5   **(d)**   How does he get to school?

....

(1 mark)

5   **(e)**   Give **two** reasons why he thinks school is OK overall.

....

....

(2 marks)

6

Read the following statements about the environment and match each one to the correct picture.

Write the correct letter in each box.

Example: Je prends toujours une douche.   H

6   **(a)**   Je vais partout à pied.   *(1 mark)*

6   **(b)**   Je me brosse les dents avec le robinet fermé.   *(1 mark)*

6   **(c)**   Je recycle le verre.   *(1 mark)*

6   **(d)**   Je déteste la pollution causée par les usines.   *(1 mark)*

7   Read this email from Simon.

Je suis très sportif. Je fais du judo trois fois par semaine et je nage tous les samedis. J'aime bien les sports d'équipe. Je joue au volley dans un club mais je ne joue plus au rugby car l'année dernière, je me suis cassé le bras pendant que j'y jouais et maintenant, je pense que c'est un sport assez dangereux. En hiver, mon frère fait du ski mais ce n'est pas mon truc. Je voudrais bien essayer le VTT un de ces jours. Mon père joue souvent au golf parce qu'il pense que c'est un bon moyen de rester en forme. Ma mère ne fait pas de sport mais elle aime regarder le tennis à la télé de temps en temps.

Decide which **four** of the following sentences are true.

Write the correct letter in each box.

A	Simon is very sporty.
B	Simon does judo twice a week.
C	Simon goes swimming once a week.
D	Simon does not play volleyball.
E	Simon used to play rugby.
F	Simon thinks that rugby is dangerous.
G	Simon goes skiing in winter.
H	Simon would like to go mountain biking.
I	Simon's brother likes golf.
J	Simon's mum plays tennis from time to time.

Example: A

7   ☐

☐

☐

☐

(4 marks)

8   Look at the dates of these events.

Il y aura un festival de musique le onze juin.
Le concert de musique classique, c'est le vingt-six avril.
La fête, c'est le vingt-huit juillet.
Les cours de danse classique commenceront le dix-neuf juillet.
Rendez-vous au restaurant le quinze juin à huit heures.
Le nouveau cinéma ouvre le seize août.

Which of the following dates are mentioned?

Write the correct **three** letters in the boxes.

A	11th June
B	11th July
C	16th August
D	19th July
E	28th April
F	26th April
G	29th July

Example: A

8

(3 marks)

TOTAL FOR PAPER IS 35 MARKS

Audio files
Audio files for the listening exercises in this book can be found at: www.pearsonschools.co.uk/mflrevisionaudio

1   Sophie is talking about her friends.

How does she describe them?

A	tall
B	small
C	medium height
D	blond hair
E	black hair
F	thin
G	green eyes
H	blue eyes

Listen and write the correct letter in each box.

Example: Louis   **F**

1   **(a)**   Romain   ☐   *(1 mark)*

1   **(b)**   Raphaël   ☐   *(1 mark)*

1   **(c)**   Maya   ☐   *(1 mark)*

1   **(d)**   Soraya   ☐   *(1 mark)*

2   Listen to these young people talking about their hobbies.

Write the correct letter in each box.

A		B	
C		D	
E		F	
G		H	
I			

Example: Paul   [C]

2   **(a)**   Léo   [ ]   *(1 mark)*

2   **(b)**   Lisa   [ ]   *(1 mark)*

2   **(c)**   Julie   [ ]   *(1 mark)*

2   **(d)**   Michel   [ ]   *(1 mark)*

2   **(e)**   Ramona   [ ]   *(1 mark)*

3   Listen to Bastien talking about his breakfast.

Answer the questions **in English**.

Example: When does he have breakfast? ....7am....

3   **(a)**   What does he usually drink?

....

(1 mark)

3   **(b)**   What does he usually eat?

....

....

(2 marks)

3   **(c)**   What does he eat when he is in a hurry?

....

(1 mark)

3   **(d)**   What does he have for breakfast at the weekend?

....

....

(2 marks)

4   Listen to these young people talking about where they live.

Write the correct letter in each box.

A	A small town in the south of France.
B	A large town in the south of France.
C	A large town in the west of France.
D	A small town in the east of France.
E	A fishing port.
F	A small town by the sea.
G	A ski resort.
H	An industrial town in the north of France.
I	A small village in the mountains.

Example: H

4   (a)   *(1 mark)*

4   (b)   *(1 mark)*

4   (c)   *(1 mark)*

4   (d)   *(1 mark)*

4   (e)   *(1 mark)*

5   Listen to Élise talking about her school.

What are her opinions about the following?

Write **P** (positive), **N** (negative) or
P/N (positive and negative) in each box.

Example: Sport at school   N

5   **(a)**   School rules   ☐   *(1 mark)*

5   **(b)**   Maths   ☐   *(1 mark)*

5   **(c)**   The canteen   ☐   *(1 mark)*

5   **(d)**   The teachers   ☐   *(1 mark)*

5   **(e)**   The classrooms   ☐   *(1 mark)*

6   Listen to Axel talking about his holidays.

Complete the sentences by choosing the correct letter.

Write the correct letter in each box.

Example: Axel usually goes to …

    A Italy   **B** Spain   **C** England   B

6   **(a)**   He normally travels by …

    A car   **B** plane   **C** boat   *(1 mark)*

6   **(b)**   Last year he went to …

    A Africa   **B** Wales   **C** Germany   *(1 mark)*

6   **(c)**   He found the staff at his hotel …

    A polite   **B** rude   **C** lazy   *(1 mark)*

6   **(d)**   Next year he is planning to …

    A visit his cousin **B** go camping   **C** stay in France   *(1 mark)*

6   **(e)**   He hopes to …

    A sunbathe   **B** take long walks   **C** go fishing   *(1 mark)*

7 Listen to these people talking about ways to combat stress.

What does each person do?

Write the correct letter in each box.

A	Watch TV
B	Go to bed
C	Eat chocolate
D	Have a bath
E	Chat to friends
F	Talk to family
G	Have a hot drink
H	Take some exercise
I	Read
J	Listen to music

Example: A

7 **(a)** [ ] *(1 mark)*

7 **(b)** [ ] *(1 mark)*

7 **(c)** [ ] *(1 mark)*

7 **(d)** [ ] *(1 mark)*

7 **(e)** [ ] *(1 mark)*

TOTAL FOR PAPER IS 35 MARKS

1   Here are some types of TV programme.

A	un film de science-fiction
B	une émission de sport
C	un documentaire
D	une émission de télé-réalité
E	un dessin animé
F	une émission de musique pop
G	un feuilleton

Which programme would each of the following select?

Write the correct letter in each box.

Example: Marc likes football.   `B`

1   **(a)**   Lily likes cartoons.   ☐   *(1 mark)*

1   **(b)**   Aimée likes documentaries.   ☐   *(1 mark)*

1   **(c)**   Samy likes reality TV programmes.   ☐   *(1 mark)*

1   **(d)**   Rémy likes soap operas.   ☐   *(1 mark)*

2	**A**	Maths		**B**	Geography	
	C	ICT		**D**	DT	
	E	PE		**F**	Chemistry	
	G	Drama				

What is each person's favourite subject?

Write the correct letter in each box.

Example: Je préfère les maths.   ☐ A

2   **(a)**   Moi, j'aime mieux l'informatique.   ☐   *(1 mark)*

2   **(b)**   Ma matière préférée, c'est la chimie.   ☐   *(1 mark)*

2   **(c)**   J'adore le théâtre.   ☐   *(1 mark)*

2   **(d)**   Je préfère la technologie.   ☐   *(1 mark)*

3   Read this email about Élodie's family.

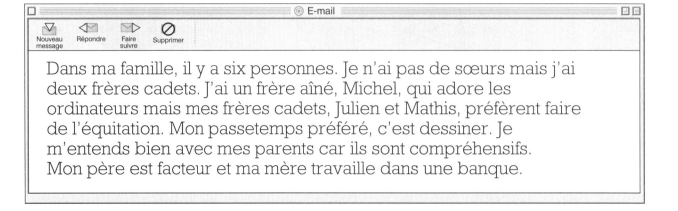

Answer the following questions.

Write the correct letter in each box.

Example: How many people are there in Élodie's family?

  A 4   **B** 5   **C** 6 | C |

3   **(a)**   How many older brothers does she have?

  A 0   **B** 1   **C** 2 | | *(1 mark)*

3   **(b)**   Why does she get on well with her parents?

  A They are   **B** They are not   **C** They are | | *(1 mark)*
      generous.   strict.   understanding.

3   **(c)**   What is her father's job?

  A a postman   **B** a factory worker   **C** a bank clerk | | *(1 mark)*

3   **(d)**   What does Michel like?

  A swimming   **B** computers   **C** cycling | | *(1 mark)*

3   **(e)**   What does Julien like?

  A swimming   **B** horse riding   **C** fishing | | *(1 mark)*

4   Read the following programme for a school exchange.

A	lundi	Excursion au parc d'attractions
B	mardi	Après-midi au centre commercial
C	mercredi	Visite du musée des voitures
D	jeudi	Journée avec les familles d'accueil
E	vendredi	Excursion au château fort
F	samedi	Journée au centre sportif municipal
G	dimanche	Fête à l'hôtel de ville

Find the correct day for these activities.

Write the correct letter in each box.

Example: Sporting activities   F

4   **(a)**   Visit to a castle   ☐   *(1 mark)*

4   **(b)**   Party in the town hall   ☐   *(1 mark)*

4   **(c)**   Shopping   ☐   *(1 mark)*

4   **(d)**   Looking at vintage cars   ☐   *(1 mark)*

5   Read these opinions about jobs.

For each one give an advantage and a disadvantage.

Write the answers **in English** in each box.

Je pense que travailler comme vendeur est facile, mais d'un autre côté, c'est ennuyeux.

Example:

Job	Advantage	Disadvantage
Shop assistant	Easy	Boring

1   Travailler comme infirmière, c'est bien, car on aide les autres, mais je sais aussi que les heures de travail sont très longues.

2   Il y a des avantages et des inconvénients à être professeur parce qu'on est bien payé mais les élèves peuvent être difficiles.

3   Je voudrais être fermier car j'adore le travail en plein air, mais j'ai peur des vaches.

Job			Advantage	Disadvantage
5	**(a)**	Nurse		
5	**(b)**	Teacher		
5	**(c)**	Farmer		

(6 marks)

6   Read this email from Anaïs.

Boîte de réception

Nouveau message   Supprimer   Répondre   Répondre à tous   Faire suivre

Salut! C'est moi, Anaïs. Tu m'as demandé de t'écrire au sujet de la santé. Je fais attention à ce que je mange. Par exemple, j'essaie de ne pas manger de bonbons et j'évite aussi les matières grasses. En plus, je bois beaucoup d'eau et je ne consomme jamais d'alcool. Il y a quelques années, j'ai essayé une cigarette, mais je ne fume pas car c'est mauvais pour la santé. Je ne suis pas sportive et je ne fais pas d'exercice physique sauf aux cours d'EPS au collège. Cependant, à l'avenir, je vais aller plus souvent à la piscine et je jouerai au squash avec mon frère.

Decide if the following sentences are T (true), F (false) or ? (not mentioned).

Example: Anaïs was asked to write about health.   `T`

6   **(a)**   Anaïs eats a lot of sweets.   ☐   *(1 mark)*

6   **(b)**   She is a vegetarian.   ☐   *(1 mark)*

6   **(c)**   She drinks alcohol from time to time.   ☐   *(1 mark)*

6   **(d)**   She tried smoking.   ☐   *(1 mark)*

6   **(e)**   She does no sports except PE at school.   ☐   *(1 mark)*

6   **(f)**   She is planning to do more swimming.   ☐   *(1 mark)*

7 Read what these three young people do to celebrate their birthdays.

Charlotte: D'habitude, pour fêter mon anniversaire, mes parents organisent une fête chez nous. Tous mes copains sont invités et on danse, on écoute de la musique et on mange bien. L'année dernière, j'ai décidé de passer la journée au parc d'attractions avec ma meilleure copine et c'était vraiment génial.

Mathilde: Moi, je n'aime pas les fêtes, alors normalement, je sors en ville avec quelques copains et on dîne ensemble dans un restaurant chinois. L'année prochaine, j'aurai dix-huit ans et mes parents vont organiser une soirée musicale avec des feux d'artifice. J'attends ça avec impatience!

Noémie: Je viens d'avoir dix-huit ans et pour mon anniversaire, j'ai passé la journée au bord de la mer avec ma famille. Ma sœur et moi avons fait de la planche à voile et c'était très amusant. L'année prochaine, mes parents vont louer une salle dans un hôtel de luxe et nous fêterons l'événement avec plein d'amis.

Answer the following questions.

Write **C** (Charlotte), **M** (Mathilde) or **N** (Noémie) in each box.

Example:	Who usually has a party for her birthday?	**C**	
7 **(a)**	Who does not like parties?		*(1 mark)*
7 **(b)**	Who has just turned 18?		*(1 mark)*
7 **(c)**	Who went windsurfing on her birthday?		*(1 mark)*
7 **(d)**	Who went out with her best friend last year?		*(1 mark)*
7 **(e)**	Who is planning to have fireworks as part of next year's celebration?		*(1 mark)*
7 **(f)**	Who usually spends her birthday at home?		*(1 mark)*

TOTAL FOR PAPER IS 35 MARKS

Audio files
Audio files for the listening exercises in this book can be found at: www.pearsonschools.co.uk/mflrevisionaudio

1   Where do these people like to go at the weekend?

Write the correct letter in each box.

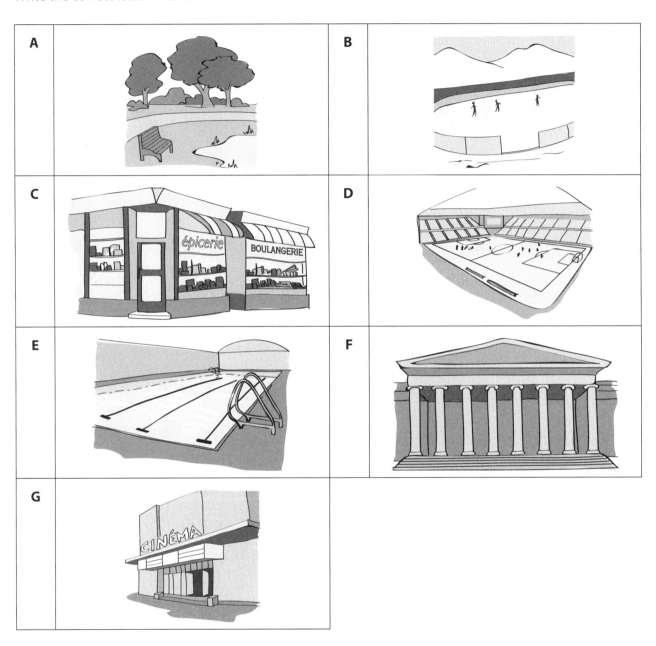

Example: G

1   **(a)** [ ]   *(1 mark)*

1   **(b)** [ ]   *(1 mark)*

1   **(c)** [ ]   *(1 mark)*

1   **(d)** [ ]   *(1 mark)*

2   Lise is talking about her work experience.

Which things does she mention?

Write the correct letter in each box.

A	her boss
B	her colleagues
C	her journey to work
D	what she did at lunchtime
E	the starting and finishing times
F	what she ate for lunch
G	her clothes
H	her plans for the future
I	her opinion of the work experience
J	her daily tasks

Example: | B |

2 | |

| |

| |

| |

| |

(5 marks)

3   Listen to Alicia talking about her friends.

Write the correct letter in each box.

A	dynamic
B	good at sport
C	generous
D	shy
E	hard-working
F	cool
G	kind
H	clever
I	talkative

Example: Pauline   A

3   **(a)**   Lucille   ☐   *(1 mark)*

3   **(b)**   Anna   ☐   *(1 mark)*

3   **(c)**   Benjamin   ☐   *(1 mark)*

3   **(d)**   Mélissa   ☐   *(1 mark)*

3   **(e)**   Abdi   ☐   *(1 mark)*

4 Listen to Tristan talking about his likes and dislikes.

Which **five** things are mentioned?

Write the correct letter in each box.

A	his favourite colour
B	games consoles
C	going to the theatre
D	skiing
E	books
F	football
G	spiders
H	roller skating
I	eating out

Example: | A |

4

(5 marks)

5   Listen to Sarah talking about her school.

Which **four** statements are true?

Write the correct letter in each box.

A	Sarah loves IT.
B	She finds chemistry interesting.
C	She likes her maths teacher.
D	Her favourite subject is art.
E	She used to like English.
F	She has French four times a week.
G	She usually goes home for lunch.
H	She thinks she has too many French lessons.
I	She has changed her opinion about history.

Example: A

5

(4 marks)

6   Listen to these young people talking about relationships.

Fill in the gaps **in English**.

Example: Camille would like to meet someone with $\underline{\text{brown eyes}}$.

6   **(a)**   Lilou would like to meet a boy who is .... and has .... hair.

(2 marks)

6   **(b)**   Léon wants to meet a girl who is .... but he thinks that her ....
is not important.

(2 marks)

6   **(c)**   Aurélie would like to meet someone who is .... but does not like people who

are ....

(2 marks)

7 What job does each person want to do?

Write the correct letter in each box.

A	vet
B	doctor
C	nurse
D	shop assistant
E	mechanic
F	policeman
G	hairdresser
H	teacher
I	gardener
J	engineer
K	IT worker

Example: | J |

7 **(a)** ☐ *(1 mark)*

7 **(b)** ☐ *(1 mark)*

7 **(c)** ☐ *(1 mark)*

7 **(d)** ☐ *(1 mark)*

7 **(e)** ☐ *(1 mark)*

7 **(f)** ☐ *(1 mark)*

TOTAL FOR PAPER IS 35 MARKS

1   Read this account of Martin's holiday.

> J'aime aller en vacances à la montagne car l'air est pur. Cependant, la semaine dernière, j'ai passé mes vacances au bord de la mer en Italie avec ma famille. J'adore partir en vacances avec mes parents car ils payent tout mais mon petit frère m'énerve, surtout en vacances.
>
> Notre hôtel était situé tout près de la plage, ce qui m'a vraiment plu. J'ai dû partager ma chambre avec mon frère ce qui m'a déplu car je ne m'entends pas bien avec lui. Mais heureusement, la chambre était grande et bien équipée.
>
> Il y avait un restaurant au sous-sol où on a mangé chaque soir. Les repas étaient formidables pour la plupart, sauf le dernier soir quand on nous a servi du poisson trop épicé. Je n'ai pas du tout aimé ça!
>
> À mon avis, la piscine de l'hôtel n'était pas propre et l'eau était froide, alors j'ai préféré me baigner dans la mer. Un jour, nous avons décidé de visiter un château dans la région. Mes parents l'ont trouvé très intéressant mais moi, je l'ai trouvé barbant.
>
> Il n'y a pas eu de problème pendant le vol de retour et nous sommes arrivés chez nous à l'heure.

What is Martin's opinion of the following?

Write **P** (positive), **N** (negative) or **P/N** (positive and negative) in each box.

Example   Mountain holidays   ☐ P

1   **(a)**   Family holidays   ☐   (1 mark)

1   **(b)**   The location of the hotel   ☐   (1 mark)

1   **(c)**   His room   ☐   (1 mark)

1   **(d)**   The meals in the restaurant   ☐   (1 mark)

1   **(e)**   The hotel pool   ☐   (1 mark)

1   **(f)**   The castle   ☐   (1 mark)

1   **(g)**   The return journey   ☐   (1 mark)

2   Read Enzo's comments about sports.

> Je suis assez actif et je sais qu'il faut faire du sport afin de rester en forme. Mon frère n'est pas sportif et il n'aime pas le sport. Il préfère rester devant son ordinateur! En hiver, je dois jouer au foot et au rugby au collège mais je n'aime pas ça car les sports d'équipe sont difficiles pour moi. Mon sport préféré, c'est le VTT mais j'aime aussi faire de la natation.
>
> Quand j'étais plus jeune, je jouais au tennis deux fois par semaine mais je n'y joue plus. Ma sœur joue bien et elle s'entraîne tous les jeudis. Mon père joue au golf de temps en temps et il fait de la planche à voile en été. Le seul exercice physique que fait ma mère, c'est du jogging.
>
> À l'avenir, j'ai l'intention de faire plus de sport. Je pense que je vais essayer de faire de la voile et aussi du ski nautique.

Complete the answers by selecting the correct letter.

Example: Enzo knows that …

A he is very sporty   **B** he should do sport to keep fit   **C** he is very fit   `B`

2 **(a)** His brother …

A is very active   **B** likes spending time on his computer   **C** loves sport   *(1 mark)*

2 **(b)** In winter Enzo …

A plays no sport   **B** watches rugby and football   **C** plays sport at school   *(1 mark)*

2 **(c)** He dislikes team sports because …

A he finds them difficult   **B** he finds them boring   **C** he hates playing against his friends   *(1 mark)*

2 **(d)** His favourite sport is …

A swimming   **B** mountain biking   **C** tennis   *(1 mark)*

2 **(e)** He used to …

A go training on Thursdays   **B** go swimming regularly   **C** play tennis twice a week   *(1 mark)*

2 **(f)** His father …

A goes jogging   **B** plays golf every day   **C** goes windsurfing in summer   *(1 mark)*

2 **(g)** In the future Enzo …

A would like to try sailing   **B** wants to do more skiing   **C** plans to do less sport   *(1 mark)*

3   Match the two halves of each sentence so that they make sense.

Write the correct letter in each box.

(a)	Moi, je voudrais travailler …	**A**	très dur.
(b)	L'année dernière, j'ai fait mon stage …	**B**	comme pompier.
(c)	Mon père travaille …	**C**	il faut trouver un emploi bien payé.
(d)	Mes parents pensent qu' …	**D**	de trouver un petit job.
(e)	Je n'ai …	**E**	dans un magasin de musique.
(f)	J'ai un petit job qui …	**F**	aucune envie d'être professeur.
(g)	Mon copain vient …	**G**	me plaît.

Example: (a)   Moi, je voudrais travailler …   ☐ B

3   **(b)**   L'année dernière, j'ai fait mon stage …   ☐   *(1 mark)*

3   **(c)**   Mon père travaille …   ☐   *(1 mark)*

3   **(d)**   Mes parents pensent qu' …   ☐   *(1 mark)*

3   **(e)**   Je n'ai …   ☐   *(1 mark)*

3   **(f)**   J'ai un petit job qui …   ☐   *(1 mark)*

3   **(g)**   Mon copain vient …   ☐   *(1 mark)*

4   Read Margot's email about her education.

Mail

Fichier   Édition   Affichage   Composer   Envoyer   Aide

Salut!

Tu m'as demandé de te parler un peu de ma vie scolaire.

Quand j'étais petite, j'allais à une école primaire qui était tout près de ma maison. À mon avis, c'était tout à fait agréable car les instituteurs étaient enthousiastes et je n'avais pas de devoirs. Je m'intéressais aux cours et je m'amusais bien, surtout pendant les cours de dessin et de lecture.

À l'âge de onze ans, je suis allée à un grand collège qui me semblait énorme. J'étais un peu malheureuse car la plupart de mes amis proches sont allés ailleurs et je me sentais isolée. J'ai trouvé les cours assez durs mais j'ai réussi à trouver de bons copains et j'ai eu de bons résultats, surtout en langues et en chimie. Mes profs étaient plus sévères que mes anciens instituteurs, mais je m'entendais bien avec mon prof d'EPS.

Margot

Answer the questions **in English**.

Example: Where was Margot's primary school? <u>Near her house.</u>

4   **(a)**   Why do you think Margot was happy at primary school? Give **two** details apart from lessons.

....

(2 marks)

4   **(b)**   Which of her lessons did she particularly like?

....

(2 marks)

4   **(c)**   Why did she feel unhappy when she started secondary school? Give **two** details.

....

(2 marks)

4   **(d)**   What did she finally manage to do? Give **two** details.

....

(2 marks)

4   **(e)**   Why could you argue that she did not feel totally against her teachers?

....

(1 mark)

5   Read Rakim's account of life in Africa.

> J'habite au Sénégal, en Afrique, depuis ma naissance. Comme dans beaucoup de pays, il y a de gros problèmes. Le chômage et la faim sont les pires. Heureusement, mon père a un emploi, donc on a assez à manger, mais j'ai peur de ne pas pouvoir trouver de travail ici plus tard.
>
> À cause de la sécheresse, on ne peut pas cultiver suffisamment de nourriture, alors on a besoin de l'aide des pays riches comme la France. Puisque je suis doué en langues, j'espère aller vivre à l'étranger à l'avenir, soit en Allemagne, soit en Belgique. Si je réussis à trouver un emploi, j'enverrai de l'argent à ma famille, comme ça tout le monde pourra déménager aussi.
>
> Mon cousin vient de partir pour aller vivre en France où il est footballeur professionnel et à mon avis, il a de la chance !

Which **five** statements are true according to the text?

Write the correct letters in each box.

A	Rakim lives in Senegal.	B	Rakim has just moved to France.
C	Unemployment is a serious problem in Senegal.	D	Rakim's father is unemployed.
E	Rakim is worried about his own future.	F	It doesn't rain much in Rakim's area of Senegal.
G	Rakim plans to learn French in the future.	H	Rakim has sent money to his family.
I	He hopes to live abroad in the future.	J	His family has recently moved house.
K	Rakim thinks his cousin is lucky.		

Example: A

5   ☐

☐

☐

☐

☐

(5 marks)

6   Read these comments about relationships.

Sarah: J'aimerais me marier un jour mais je sais que je voudrais aller à l'université avant. J'ai un petit ami depuis trois ans mais je ne sais pas si nous serons ensemble plus tard. Quant aux enfants, j'en voudrais deux, un garçon et une fille.

Delphine: Je suis contre le mariage parce que je voudrais rester indépendante. Néanmoins, je crois que j'aurai un compagnon un jour et mon compagnon idéal aurait les mêmes goûts et les mêmes centres d'intérêt que moi. Cependant, je n'aimerais pas avoir d'enfants.

Juliette: Moi, je ne sais pas si je me marierai à l'avenir mais je suis sûre que j'aimerais avoir plusieurs enfants. Mes parents sont divorcés et quand j'étais jeune, ils se sont beaucoup disputés, ce qui m'énervait énormément. J'étais souvent triste à cause de leurs disputes. Je viens de rencontrer un garçon qui me plaît, mais je ne pense pas qu'on restera ensemble.

Answer the following questions.

Write **S** (Sarah), **D** (Delphine) or **J** (Juliette) in each box.

Example: Who wants to get married in the future?   S

6   **(a)**   Who does not want children?   (1 mark)

6   **(b)**   Who has been in a steady relationship for some time?   (1 mark)

6   **(c)**   Who wants an education before marrying?   (1 mark)

6   **(d)**   Who has just met a boy she likes?   (1 mark)

6   **(e)**   Who was unhappy when she was younger?   (1 mark)

6   **(f)**   Who would like to find someone who shares her tastes?   (1 mark)

TOTAL FOR PAPER IS 40 MARKS

Audio files
Audio files for the listening exercises in this book can be found at: www.pearsonschools.co.uk/mflrevisionaudio

1 Listen to these young people talking about where they live.

For each person give a positive and negative of where they live.

Answer the questions **in English**.

	☺	☹
Example:	Near school	No ice rink
1 **(a)**		
1 **(b)**		
1 **(c)**		

(6 marks)

2   Listen to these young people's opinions about TV programmes.

For each one write **P** (positive opinion), **N** (negative opinion) or **P/N** (positive and negative opinion) in each box.

Example: [N]

2   **(a)**   [   ]   *(1 mark)*

2   **(b)**   [   ]   *(1 mark)*

2   **(c)**   [   ]   *(1 mark)*

2   **(d)**   [   ]   *(1 mark)*

3   Listen to the following people discussing their future plans.

Find the most suitable job in the list.

For each person, write the correct letter in each box.

A	doctor
B	hairdresser
C	mechanic
D	chef
E	police officer
F	secretary
G	shop assistant
H	farmer
I	greengrocer
J	postman

Example: G

3   **(a)**   ☐   *(1 mark)*

3   **(b)**   ☐   *(1 mark)*

3   **(c)**   ☐   *(1 mark)*

3   **(d)**   ☐   *(1 mark)*

3   **(e)**   ☐   *(1 mark)*

4   Listen to Clément and Safia talking about technology.

Answer the questions.

Write the correct letter in each box.

Example: How old is Clément?

A   15   B   16   C   17 | B |

Part 1   Answer questions **4 (a)–4 (c).**

4   **(a)**   What is the main reason Clément uses his mobile phone?

A   to text his   B   to let his parents   C   to take photos
    friends   know that he is
                             running late

(1 mark)

4   **(b)**   How does he describe his new phone?

A   very small   B   the latest model   C   the best model   *(1 mark)*

4   **(c)**   What does he plan to use his phone to do in the future?

A   listen to music   B   watch videos   C   get sports results   *(1 mark)*

Part 2   Answer questions **4 (d)–4 (f).**

4   **(d)**   Why does Safia prefer to use a word processor?

A   she has poor   B   it's easier   C   she thinks it's more   *(1 mark)*
    handwriting   formal

4   **(e)**   What has happened as a result of Safia using chatrooms?

A   she has done   B   she has had her   C   she has made friends   *(1 mark)*
    less sport   identity stolen

4   **(f)**   How often does she check her emails?

A   once an hour   B   once a day   C   every 10 minutes   *(1 mark)*

5   Listen to Almeira talking about her life.

Answer the questions **in English**.

Example: Where does Almeira live? .Togo.

Part 1   Answer questions **5 (a) and 5 (b).**

5   **(a)**   Which **two** problems does Almeira mention about Togo?

....

....

(2 marks)

5   **(b)**   Why is life now a little easier for Almeira's family?

....

(1 mark)

Part 2   Answer questions **5 (c) and 5 (d).**

5   **(c)**   Which **two** industries used to flourish in Lomé?

....

....

(2 marks)

5   **(d)**   What has Almeira's brother decided to do?

....

....

(2 marks)

Part 3   Answer questions **5 (e) and 5 (f).**

5   **(e)**   What makes Almeira pessimistic for her future?

....

(1 mark)

5   **(f)**   Which **two** environmental problems does she mention?

....

....

(2 marks)

6   Listen to Jasmine talking about holidays.

A	Jasmine prefers active holidays.	B	Her sister loves sunbathing.
C	Her brother was sick on holiday last year.	D	Jasmine is afraid of flying.
E	Jasmine would like to visit America.	F	Her dad has never been abroad.
G	Her mum loves museums.	H	Jasmine has never been skiing.
I	Her sister likes swimming.	J	Jasmine hates camping.
K	Her mum has been to Switzerland.	L	Jasmine prefers holidays with friends.

Find the **five** correct statements according to the text.

Write the correct letter in each box.

Example: A

6

(5 marks)

7   Listen to Paul talking about pocket money.

A	tidy his room
B	go shopping for his grandfather
C	help out at a youth club
D	mow the lawn
E	walk the neighbour's dog
F	look after the neighbour's cats
G	get good marks at school
H	buy computer games
I	buy clothes
J	go out with friends

Which **four** things has Paul done?

Write the correct letter in each box.

Example: ┌─────┐
                │ A │
                └─────┘

7   ┌─────┐
                │   │
                └─────┘

                ┌─────┐
                │   │
                └─────┘

                ┌─────┐
                │   │
                └─────┘

                ┌─────┐
                │   │
                └─────┘

(4 marks)

TOTAL FOR PAPER IS 40 MARKS

1   Read Armand's comments about where he lives.

J'habite dans un HLM dans la banlieue de Paris. C'est un quartier qui était chic avant mais maintenant, ce n'est plus très populaire. Comme dans toutes les grandes villes, il y a des problèmes environnementaux comme la pollution car il y a plein de camions qui font des livraisons et les embouteillages sont nombreux, surtout aux heures de pointe.

Bien sûr, il y a des zones piétonnes, mais je pense qu'il faut créer plus d'espaces verts. En plus, je pense qu'il faudrait obliger les automobilistes à payer s'ils veulent entrer dans le centre-ville, comme ça on réduirait non seulement le nombre de véhicules en ville mais aussi les gaz d'échappement.

For each sentence write **T** (true), **F** (false) or **?** (not mentioned) in each box.

Example: Armand lives in a house.   F

1 **(a)**   He lives in a smart area of Paris.   ☐   *(1 mark)*

1 **(b)**   He thinks that Paris has the same problems as other cities.   ☐   *(1 mark)*

1 **(c)**   He thinks that lorries are partly to blame for pollution.   ☐   *(1 mark)*

1 **(d)**   He thinks that Paris is an affluent place.   ☐   *(1 mark)*

1 **(e)**   There are pedestrian zones in Paris.   ☐   *(1 mark)*

1 **(f)**   He thinks there should be more cycle paths.   ☐   *(1 mark)*

1 **(g)**   He believes that motorists should pay to enter the city.   ☐   *(1 mark)*

2   Read these job adverts.

A	Nous cherchons un vendeur pour notre magasin de vêtements au centre-ville. Salaire: 12 euros par heure. Weekends de 9h à 17h.
B	On cherche serveur/serveuse pour un restaurant intime et chaleureux, situé près de la gare. Travail tous les jours sauf le vendredi. Pourboires partagés entre le personnel.
C	Propriétaire d'une nouvelle entreprise commerciale cherche secrétaire. Expérience essentielle. Salaire à négocier. Lundi–vendredi.
D	On cherche quelqu'un pour nettoyer le centre sportif tous les soirs de 20h à 22h sauf le dimanche. Salaire: dix euros par heure.
E	Supermarché Pascal cherche boulanger, plus de dix-huit ans. Travail tous les matins de 5h à 8h. 7 euros par heure.

Which advert mentions the following?

Write the correct letter in the box.

Example: supermarket work   E

2   **(a)**   working as a cleaner   ☐   *(1 mark)*

2   **(b)**   working every day   ☐   *(1 mark)*

2   **(c)**   working near the station   ☐   *(1 mark)*

2   **(d)**   selling clothes   ☐   *(1 mark)*

2   **(e)**   working as a baker   ☐   *(1 mark)*

2   **(f)**   tips shared   ☐   *(1 mark)*

2   **(g)**   salary to be decided   ☐   *(1 mark)*

2   **(h)**   working for a new company   ☐   *(1 mark)*

3   Read this article about Jean's lifestyle.

> Je réussis à résister à presque toutes sortes de friandises mais j'adore le chocolat, même si je sais que c'est mauvais pour la santé. Tous les jours, je prends un petit déjeuner copieux car c'est important de bien manger le matin. Des fois, je suis pressé, mais je ne saute jamais ce repas essentiel. Par contre, je ne prends qu'un déjeuner léger, soit des framboises ou des prunes, soit des noix. Le soir, on mange toujours à table en famille mais j'essaie de limiter ma consommation de viande rouge.
>
> J'ai plein de copains qui boivent de l'alcool mais moi, je n'en bois pas car avoir la forme, c'est important pour moi. J'évite les boissons gazeuses et je bois beaucoup d'eau parce que c'est bon pour la peau.

Answer the questions **in English**.

Example: What can Jean not resist eating?   *chocolate*

3   **(a)**   Why do you think that Jean's morning routine is healthy? Give **two** details.

....

(2 marks)

3   **(b)**   What does he have for lunch? Name any **two** items.

....

(2 marks)

3   **(c)**   Why do you think that Jean's family has traditional values?

....

(1 mark)

3   **(d)**   What type of food is Jean trying to limit?

....

(1 mark)

3   **(e)**   What **two** types of drink does Jean avoid drinking?

....

(2 marks)

3   **(f)**   Why does he drink lots of water?

....

(1 mark)

4   Read this letter.

> Hier soir, je suis allée manger dans votre restaurant «Le Toulousain» avec ma famille. Nous étions très déçus car nous avons eu plusieurs problèmes. D'abord, mon père avait réservé une table pour sept heures trente, mais on a dû attendre un quart d'heure au bar avant de pouvoir dîner. Le service était lent et la serveuse n'était pas très polie. En plus, j'ai choisi du poulet rôti avec des haricots verts mais tout était froid! Il n'y avait plus de tarte aux pommes, ce qui a beaucoup embêté ma mère, et le café qu'on nous a servi était trop fort.
>
> Je ne reviendrai pas.
>
> Sandrine Dumoulin

Answer the questions.

Put the correct letter in each box.

Example: When did Sandrine go to the restaurant?

    A   last week   **B**   last month   **C**   yesterday | C |

4   **(a)**   How did the family feel at the end of the meal?

    A   angry   **B**   disappointed   **C**   happy   *(1 mark)*

4   **(b)**   When did they sit down to eat?

    A   7:30   **B**   7:45   **C**   8:00   *(1 mark)*

4   **(c)**   What did Sandrine say about the service?

    A   it was acceptable   **B**   the waitress was polite   **C**   it was slow   *(1 mark)*

4   **(d)**   What was wrong with her meal?

    A   it was too spicy   **B**   it was not warm enough   **C**   it had the wrong vegetables   *(1 mark)*

4   **(e)**   What annoyed her mother?

    A   the dessert she wanted was unavailable   **B**   she was allergic to the apples   **C**   her tart tasted bad   *(1 mark)*

4   **(f)**   What was wrong with the coffee?

    A   it was cold when it arrived   **B**   there was no milk   **C**   it was too strong   *(1 mark)*

5   Read Marc's comments about smoking.

> Je ne fumerai jamais puisque je n'ai aucune envie de devenir accro au tabac. Avant, ma tante fumait mais elle a arrêté il y a six mois. Elle était souvent hors d'haleine mais maintenant, elle va mieux et elle vient de s'inscrire à une salle de gym. Je suis pour les campagnes anti-tabac en France parce que trop de jeunes fument, et selon un sondage récent, les Français commencent à fumer de plus en plus tôt.

Which of the following does he mention?

Write the correct letter in each box.

A	His reason for never smoking
B	His uncle's problems with smoking
C	A family member's success story
D	His aunt's future plans to join a gym
E	Campaigns to stop French people smoking
F	His attempts to give up smoking
G	His support for anti-smoking programmes
H	At what age French people start smoking

Example: ☐ G

5   ☐

☐

☐

☐

(4 marks)

6   Select the correct word from the table below to fill each gap.

Write the correct letter in each box.

A	vais
B	voudrais
C	ferai
D	devenir
E	aller
F	suis
G	épouser
H	aimerait
I	vont
J	voyager
K	payé
L	avoir

Example: Je ☐A☐ continuer mes études au lycée l'année prochaine.

6   **(a)**   Plus tard, dans la vie, je voudrais ☐ informaticien.   *(1 mark)*

6   **(b)**   Après ☐ fini mes études, je chercherai un emploi.   *(1 mark)*

6   **(c)**   Mon copain ☐ aller à l'université.   *(1 mark)*

6   **(d)**   Je ☐ le tour du monde en avion.   *(1 mark)*

6   **(e)**   Mon rêve est de trouver un emploi bien ☐ , comme ça j'aurai assez d'argent.   *(1 mark)*

6   **(f)**   Ma sœur a l'intention d'☐ un homme riche, plus tard.   *(1 mark)*

TOTAL FOR PAPER IS 40 MARKS

Audio files
Audio files for the listening exercises in this book can be found at: www.pearsonschools.co.uk/mflrevisionaudio

Set D   Listening   Higher 2

1 Listen to these young people talking about their leisure activities.

For each person, choose an answer from each box.

Write the letters in the correct boxes.

	Activities	Time	
A	fishing	(i)	next Saturday
B	windsurfing	(ii)	last Sunday
C	shopping	(iii)	18h30
D	sailing	(iv)	8h30
E	chess	(v)	next month
F	ice skating	(vi)	16h30
G	swimming	(vii)	last week
H	horse riding	(viii)	16h45

	Activities	Time
Example:	E	iv
1 (a)		
1 (b)		
1 (c)		
1 (d)		

(8 marks)

2   Which special occasion is being discussed?

Write the correct letter in each box.

A	Easter
B	New Year's Day
C	A birthday
D	All Saints' Day
E	New Year's Eve
F	Christmas Eve
G	Christmas Day
H	A wedding
I	A christening
J	An engagement

Example: F

2   **(a)**

2   **(b)**

2   **(c)**

2   **(d)**

2   **(e)**   *(5 marks)*

3   Listen to these people discussing problems at work.

Answer the questions **in English**.

Part 1   Answer questions **3 (a)–3 (c).**

Example: Where does Aline work? In a hypermarket.

3   (a)   What were the young people trying to do and how were they trying to do this?

....

....

(2 marks)

3   (b)   What action did Aline take?

....

(1 mark)

3   (c)   What finally happened as the young people were leaving the shop?

....

(1 mark)

Part 2   Answer questions **3 (d)–3 (g).**

3   (d)   What is Marc's job?

....

(1 mark)

3   (e)   Why had he been called out by the old lady?

....

....

(2 marks)

3   (f)   What happened to Marc?

....

(1 mark)

3   (g)   What was his colleagues' reaction?

....

(1 mark)

4   Michel is talking to his friend, Lola.

Which of the statements are correct?

Write the **five** letters in the boxes.

A	Michel is looking for some shorts.	B	Michel thinks the yellow shorts are too expensive.
C	Michel thinks the blue shorts are too short.	D	Lola likes the striped skirt best.
E	Lola wants a skirt to wear at a party.	F	Michel thinks she should try the skirt on.
G	They both decide to buy an item of clothing.	H	Lola ends up buying the red skirt.
I	Lola has forgotten her purse.	J	The shop is about to close.

Example: A

4

(5 marks)

5   Listen to Ellie talking about holidays.

For each holiday write a like and dislike.

Write the correct letters in the boxes.

A	clean air
B	luxury
C	weather
D	delays
E	views
F	cost
G	local inhabitants
H	noise
I	food
J	friends
K	activities
L	museums

Example:

Holiday	☺	☹
Example: France	A	H

Holiday	☺	☹
5 **(a)** Spain		
5 **(b)** Paris		
5 **(c)** Switzerland		

(6 marks)

6 Listen to some people talking about relationships.

Answer the questions.

Write the correct letter in each box.

Example: What does Romain think of his stepfather?

      A He is generous. **B** He is strict.   **C** He is lazy.

             B

Part 1 Listen to Romain talking about relationships.

Answer questions **6 (a)–6 (c)**.

6 **(a)** For how long have Romain's parents been divorced?

      A 8 months   **B** 10 months   **C** more than a year   *(1 mark)*

6 **(b)** What does Romain say about his mum?

      A She lives   **B** She lives in   **C** He misses her.   *(1 mark)*
           close by.   Germany.

6 **(c)** Which fact annoys Romain?

      A He cannot   **B** His dad does   **C** His dad has   *(1 mark)*
           find a job.   nothing.   remarried.

Part 2 Listen to Ambre talking about her relationships.

Answer questions **6 (d) and 6 (e)**.

6 **(d)** Why does Ambre not want to go to the party?

      A She will not   **B** She has nothing   **C** Her parents will   *(1 mark)*
           know anyone   suitable to wear.   be there.
           there.

6 **(e)** Why has she recently split up with her boyfriend?

      A He had started **B** He was too   **C** He moved to a   *(1 mark)*
           to see another   possessive.   different town.
           girl.

Part 3 Now listen to Éloïse talking about her family problems.

Answer questions **6 (f) and 6 (g)**.

6 **(f)** What has happened to Éloïse?

      A She had an   **B** She argued   **C** She had problems   *(1 mark)*
           argument with   with her sister.   at school.
           her mum.

6 **(g)** What does she now regret?

      A making   **B** getting angry   **C** throwing food   *(1 mark)*
           someone cry

                                             TOTAL FOR PAPER IS 40 MARKS

1 Read what these three young people say about the environment.

Cécile: Pour moi, la protection de l'environnement est très importante. J'habite dans une grande ville industrielle où la pollution est un problème grave parce qu'il y a plein d'usines qui rejettent de la fumée dans l'air. J'ai écrit au commissaire européen à l'Environnement mais je n'ai pas eu de réponse. C'est scandaleux! Je fais ce que je peux pour aider et je recycle le verre et les journaux.

Marianne: Moi, la protection de l'environnement, ça ne m'intéresse pas vraiment et à mon avis, c'est la responsabilité de notre gouvernement. Je ne recycle rien, cependant, j'utilise souvent les transports en commun au lieu de me déplacer en voiture. Le mois dernier, j'ai persuadé mon père d'acheter une nouvelle voiture hybride. Selon moi, rien ne changera vraiment à l'avenir car beaucoup de gens sont comme moi.

Élodie: Je suis triste quand je vois des gens jeter des papiers dans la rue, même quand il y a une poubelle tout près. De plus, je pense qu'il est important d'essayer de protéger les espèces en voie de disparition, alors j'ai adopté un tigre et je vais m'inscrire dans une association qui lutte contre la cruauté envers les animaux.

Who expresses the following ideas?

Write **C** (Cécile), **M** (Marianne) or **E** (Élodie).

Example: I'm not interested in the environment.   **M**

1   **(a)**   I get upset by seeing litter.   ☐   *(1 mark)*

1   **(b)**   Many others share my views.   ☐   *(1 mark)*

1   **(c)**   I'm concerned about factories.   ☐   *(1 mark)*

1   **(d)**   I recycle glass.   ☐   *(1 mark)*

1   **(e)**   I'm going to join a society.   ☐   *(1 mark)*

1   **(f)**   I have made a written complaint.   ☐   *(1 mark)*

1   **(g)**   I think the authorities should take action.   ☐   *(1 mark)*

2   Read Mohammed's email about his school.

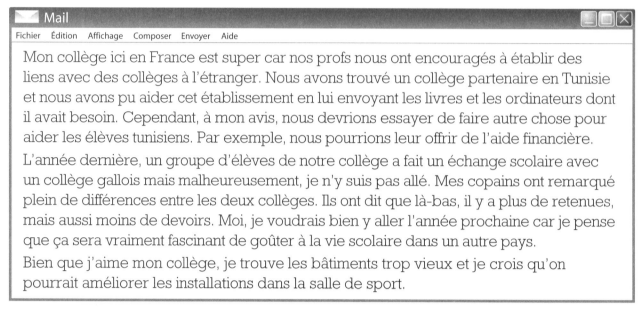

Mail

Fichier   Édition   Affichage   Composer   Envoyer   Aide

Mon collège ici en France est super car nos profs nous ont encouragés à établir des liens avec des collèges à l'étranger. Nous avons trouvé un collège partenaire en Tunisie et nous avons pu aider cet établissement en lui envoyant les livres et les ordinateurs dont il avait besoin. Cependant, à mon avis, nous devrions essayer de faire autre chose pour aider les élèves tunisiens. Par exemple, nous pourrions leur offrir de l'aide financière.

L'année dernière, un groupe d'élèves de notre collège a fait un échange scolaire avec un collège gallois mais malheureusement, je n'y suis pas allé. Mes copains ont remarqué plein de différences entre les deux collèges. Ils ont dit que là-bas, il y a plus de retenues, mais aussi moins de devoirs. Moi, je voudrais bien y aller l'année prochaine car je pense que ça sera vraiment fascinant de goûter à la vie scolaire dans un autre pays.

Bien que j'aime mon collège, je trouve les bâtiments trop vieux et je crois qu'on pourrait améliorer les installations dans la salle de sport.

Which **five** statements are true?

Write the correct letters in each box.

A	Mohammed likes his school.	B	His school is hoping to be twinned with a school in Tunisia.
C	Mohammed's school has sent IT equipment to another school.	D	His school has an exchange with an English school.
E	Mohammed thinks his school could do more to help pupils in Tunisia.	F	Mohammed has been on a school exchange.
G	The French pupils get more homework than those in the exchange school.	H	Mohammed's school gives more detentions than the exchange school.
I	Mohammed would like to see what life in a school abroad is like.	J	Mohammed thinks his school's buildings are up-to-date.
K	He would like to see better sports facilities.		

Example: A

2   ☐

☐

☐

☐

☐

(5 marks)

3   Read Antoine's account of a shopping trip.

> La semaine dernière, je suis allé en ville et j'ai fait les magasins tout seul. J'avais décidé d'acheter des cadeaux pour mon frère qui va bientôt avoir seize ans, et pour ma mère qui va célébrer son anniversaire la semaine prochaine. Mon père m'a emmené au centre-ville en voiture avant d'aller à son bureau et j'ai cherché en vain le roman que mon frère veut lire. J'ai réussi à trouver un maillot de foot de son équipe préférée et je l'ai acheté à un prix raisonnable.
>
> Après avoir pris un déjeuner rapide dans un café, je suis entré dans une bijouterie où j'ai passé une demi-heure à chercher une bague en argent pour ma mère, mais sans succès. Vers trois heures de l'après-midi, je passais devant un magasin de vêtements quand j'ai remarqué une belle écharpe en soie et j'ai téléphoné à ma sœur pour lui demander son opinion. Elle m'a dit de l'acheter, alors j'étais vraiment ravi d'avoir trouvé deux cadeaux pour ma famille!

Answer the following questions.

Write the correct letter in each box.

Example: The shopping trip took place …

| | **A** last month | **B** yesterday | **C** last week | C |

3   **(a)**   Antoine went into town to buy …

| | **A** presents for members of his family | **B** something for his father | **C** a treat for himself | | *(1 mark)* |

3   **(b)**   His brother is currently …

| | **A** 16 | **B** 15 | **C** 17 | | *(1 mark)* |

3   **(c)**   He went into town …

| | **A** on foot | **B** by bus | **C** by car | | *(1 mark)* |

3   **(d)**   For his brother Antoine bought …

| | **A** a novel | **B** a football shirt | **C** a football | | *(1 mark)* |

3   **(e)**   Antoine spent 30 minutes …

| | **A** having lunch | **B** in a clothes' shop | **C** in a jeweller's shop | | *(1 mark)* |

3   **(f)**   For his mother Antoine bought …

| | **A** a scarf | **B** a purse | **C** some perfume | | *(1 mark)* |

4   Read these comments about healthy lifestyles.

      Fill in the gaps using a word from the box.

      Write the correct letter.

A	éviter	**B**	ferons
C	jamais	**D**	sport
E	eau	**F**	légumes
G	renoncer	**H**	arrêter
I	allons	**J**	viens
K	vais	**L**	vient
M	trop	**N**	risquent
O	cancer		

Example: À mon avis, il faut faire du ...D... afin de garder la forme.

4   **(a)**   Pour être en meilleure forme, il vaudrait mieux .... le fastfood.   *(1 mark)*

4   **(b)**   Mon copain .... de commencer à aller au centre sportif deux fois par semaine.   *(1 mark)*

4   **(c)**   Ma mère mangeait .... de frites mais maintenant, elle en mange rarement.   *(1 mark)*

4   **(d)**   Mon frère et moi .... faire du jogging ensemble à l'avenir.   *(1 mark)*

4   **(e)**   Je vais essayer de boire plus d' .... car c'est bon pour la peau.   *(1 mark)*

4   **(f)**   Je fumais dix cigarettes par jour mais j'ai réussi à .... au tabac.   *(1 mark)*

4   **(g)**   Je ne prendrai .... de drogues.   *(1 mark)*

4   **(h)**   Ceux qui boivent beaucoup d'alcool .... d'endommager leur santé.   *(1 mark)*

5   Read Arthur's blog about the Internet.

> Je trouve qu'en général, Internet est super mais il y a des choses qui m'inquiètent. Voici ce que j'en pense!
>
> Je pense qu'Internet est indispensable quand on doit faire des recherches scolaires. Je peux tout trouver sans perdre de temps. Il est vrai qu'on peut faire des achats sur Internet sans quitter la maison et que beaucoup d'articles coûtent plus cher dans les magasins. Pourtant, j'aime bien pouvoir essayer des vêtements avant de les acheter.
>
> Ce qui me plaît vraiment, c'est que je peux bavarder avec mes amis et avec mon frère qui habite au Cameroun depuis deux ans sans utiliser mon téléphone. Par contre, je pense qu'il faut faire attention quand on parle à des inconnus sur un forum car il ne faut pas leur donner nos renseignements personnels, c'est nul.

What does Arthur feel about the following?

For each one write **P** (positive), **N** (negative) or **P/N** (positive and negative) in each box.

Example: the Internet   P/N

5   **(a)**   using the Internet for schoolwork   ☐   *(1 mark)*

5   **(b)**   shopping online   ☐   *(1 mark)*

5   **(c)**   staying in touch with people online   ☐   *(1 mark)*

5   **(d)**   using chatrooms   ☐   *(1 mark)*

6   Read the following headlines from the media.

A	Tensions rise in East Africa
B	Televised debate on green issues
C	Funding problems hit schools
D	Increase in crime
E	Celebrities to marry
F	Weather problems
G	Fire wrecks building
H	Deforestation a major problem

Which headline goes with each description?

Write the correct letter in each box.

Example: Les chefs d'État des pays européens vont discuter des problèmes   **B**
environnementaux à la télé ce soir.

6   **(a)**   Des vents épouvantables ont causé des dégâts sérieux au Sénégal.   *(1 mark)*

6   **(b)**   Un incendie a détruit un bâtiment au centre de Nice.   *(1 mark)*

6   **(c)**   Le chanteur DJ Rapide va épouser la vedette Léa en été.   *(1 mark)*

6   **(d)**   Le taux de criminalité continue à augmenter.   *(1 mark)*

7 Read Alice's account of her part-time job.

> Le mois dernier, j'ai trouvé un petit job dans la ville où j'habite. J'ai besoin d'argent supplémentaire car je vais payer mes frais universitaires pour l'année prochaine, donc j'étais vraiment heureuse de voir une petite annonce à l'hôtel de ville. On cherchait quelqu'un pour travailler dans une agence de voyage et, après un entretien, on m'a offert le poste.
>
> Après deux jours de formation, j'étais prête à commencer. J'ai tout de suite aimé mon travail car le contact avec le public me plaît énormément, et comme j'ai déjà fait plein de voyages à l'étranger, j'ai pu aider les gens à choisir leur destination de vacances. Avant-hier une vieille dame est entrée dans l'agence et m'a demandé d'organiser les vacances de ses rêves. Elle était très heureuse quand nous avons réussi à trouver une croisière de luxe aux Caraïbes!

Answer the questions **in English**.

Example: When did Alice get her part-time job? <u>Last month</u>

7 **(a)** Why did Alice need extra money?

....

(1 mark)

7 **(b)** Where did she see the advert for the job?

....

(1 mark)

7 **(c)** What took two days?

....

(1 mark)

7 **(d)** What **two** things did Alice think would make her a suitable candidate for the job?

....

....

(2 marks)

7 **(e)** Why do you think the old lady was happy?

....

(1 mark)

TOTAL FOR PAPER IS 40 MARKS

Audio files
Audio files for the listening exercises in this book can be found at: www.pearsonschools.co.uk/mflrevisionaudio

LISTENING 5

1   Listen to these people discussing acts at a talent show.

For each act, write the letter of the act and the speaker's opinion of the act.

For each opinion, write P (positive), N (negative) or P/N (positive and negative) in each box.

A		B	
C		D	
E		F	
G		H	
I		J	

Letter of act		Opinion		Letter of act		Opinion
Example:	F	N				
1 (a)				1 (c)		
1 (b)				1 (d)		

(8 marks)

2   Listen to this extract from a reality TV show about house renovations.

A	the living room
B	the garden
C	the loft
D	the downstairs toilet
E	the upstairs toilet
F	the dining room
G	the master bedroom
H	the shower room
I	the guest bedroom
J	the bathroom
K	the entrance hall
L	the kitchen

Which **two** areas of these homes have been renovated?

Write the correct letters in the boxes.

Example: D   F

2   **(a)**

2   **(b)**

2   **(c)**

2   **(d)**   *(8 marks)*

3   Listen to these young French people, Marc, Loïc and Sandrine talking about holidays.

Who would say each of the following?

Write M (Marc), L (Loïc) or S (Sandrine) in the correct boxes.

Example: I went on holiday with my aunt.   M

3   **(a)**   I want to sunbathe.   *(1 mark)*

3   **(b)**   The weather caused a problem on my last holiday.   *(1 mark)*

3   **(c)**   I visit a relative during the holidays.   *(1 mark)*

3   **(d)**   I like water sports.   *(1 mark)*

3   **(e)**   I have been to America recently.   *(1 mark)*

3   **(f)**   My father works abroad.   *(1 mark)*

4   Listen to the following extracts.

Where does each one take place?

Write the correct letter in each box.

A	hotel
B	campsite
C	tourist office
D	chemist's
E	library
F	castle
G	lost property office
H	supermarket
I	museum
J	police station

Example: D

4   **(a)**   (1 mark)

4   **(b)**   (1 mark)

4   **(c)**   (1 mark)

4   **(d)**   (1 mark)

5   Listen to Alex talking about his job.

Answer the questions **in English**.

Example: In which city does Alex work? Marseille

Part 1   Answer questions **5 (a)–5 (c).**

5   **(a)**   For how long has Alex worked for the organisation?

....

(1 mark)

5   **(b)**   Whom does the charity help?

....

(1 mark)

5   **(c)**   From what Alex says, what makes you think that the charity is not large?

....

(1 mark)

Part 2   Answer questions **5 (d)–5 (g).**

5   **(d)**   How many days off per week does Alex get?

....

(1 mark)

5   **(e)**   What was he doing yesterday?

....

(1 mark)

5   **(f)**   Give **three** details about the woman Alex met.

....

....

....

(3 marks)

5   **(g)**   Why is Alex still concerned about the woman at the end?

....

(1 mark)

6   Listen to Kathy talking to Clément.

Decide which statements about Kathy are true.

Write the **five** correct letters in the boxes.

A	She has no friends except Clément.
B	She has had an argument with her friend Chloé.
C	Her teachers have criticised her.
D	She never uses social network sites.
E	She feels let down by Chloé.
F	She has been accused by Chloé of cheating in an exam.
G	She will be discussing her problems with her mother tomorrow.
H	She is going to complain to her headteacher.
I	Her friend Chloé is sorry for her actions.
J	She has an appointment for tomorrow afternoon.
K	She may leave her school.
L	Chloé thinks she is stupid.

Example: B

6

(5 marks)

TOTAL FOR PAPER IS 40 MARKS

1   Read the following signs in a French town.

Write the correct letter in each box.

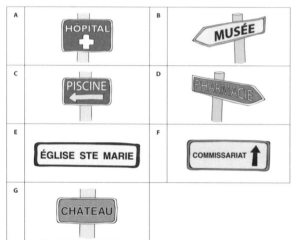

Example: You want to get some painkillers.   `D`

1   **(a)**   You want to visit a castle.   `G`   ✓   *(1 mark)*

1   **(b)**   You would like to go swimming.   `C`   ✓   *(1 mark)*

1   **(c)**   You are looking for a church.   `E`   ✓   *(1 mark)*

1   **(d)**   You want to report a theft.   `F`   ✓   *(1 mark)*

1

---

2   Read the following comments about hobbies.

A	J'adore faire du vélo.
B	Je regarde souvent la télé.
C	La natation m'intéresse beaucoup.
D	La lecture, c'est génial.
E	Ma passion, c'est jouer aux échecs.
F	J'aime bien faire les magasins.
G	J'aime beaucoup jouer sur mon ordinateur.

> Cognates are words which are the same in both English and French. Near cognates can also help you to work out the meaning of words.

Which hobby is mentioned?

Write the correct letter in each box.

Example: Watching TV   `B`

2   **(a)**   Reading   `D`   ✓   *(1 mark)*

2   **(b)**   Chess   `E`   ✓   *(1 mark)*

2   **(c)**   Cycling   `A`   ✓   *(1 mark)*

2   **(d)**   Shopping   `F`   ✓   *(1 mark)*

2

How do the following young people earn pocket money?

Write the correct letter in each box.

> Remember that sometimes recognising just one word in a sentence might allow you to come up with the correct answer.

Example: Je fais du babysitting pour ma tante.   `A`

3   **(a)**   Je travaille dans le jardin.   `C`   ✓   *(1 mark)*

3   **(b)**   Moi, je dois promener le chien.   `B`   ✓   *(1 mark)*

3   **(c)**   Je prépare le repas du soir tous les jours.   `E`   ✓   *(1 mark)*

3   **(d)**   Le samedi, je lave la voiture de ma mère.   `F`   ✓   *(1 mark)*

3

---

4   Read these young people's views on holidays.

 Léa: Moi, j'aime bien passer mes vacances au bord de la mer car je trouve ça relaxant. L'année dernière, je suis allée en Espagne avec quelques copines et nous avons fait de la planche à voile pour la première fois. C'était difficile mais marrant. L'année prochaine, je vais aller en Angleterre parce que je voudrais perfectionner mon anglais.

 Mylène: Je pars souvent en vacances avec ma famille mais nous ne logeons jamais dans un hôtel car c'est très cher. Nous faisons toujours du camping et j'aime ça. Nous venons de rentrer de nos vacances en Allemagne où nous nous sommes vraiment bien amusés.

 Chloé: Normalement, je passe mes vacances dans le sud de la France, chez mon grand-père. Il habite dans une grande ferme. Il y a un terrain de camping bien équipé en face d'une école mais je loge chez lui à la ferme. L'année prochaine, j'irai en Allemagne avec un groupe scolaire et j'espère qu'il fera beau. Nous logerons dans un petit hôtel au centre-ville.

Answer the following questions.

Write **L** (Léa), **M** (Mylène) or **C** (Chloé) in each box.

Example: Who likes going to the seaside?   `L`

4   **(a)**   Who has just returned from holidays in Germany?   `M`   ✓   *(1 mark)*

4   **(b)**   Who never stays in a hotel on holiday?   `M`   ✓   *(1 mark)*

4   **(c)**   Who is going on a school trip next year?   `C`   ✓   *(1 mark)*

4   **(d)**   Who tried a new sport last year?   `L`   ✓   *(1 mark)*

4   **(e)**   Who is hoping to improve her language skills by going on holiday?   `L`   ✓   *(1 mark)*

> Remember that finding the correct tense of the verb can sometimes help you to locate the right answer. Be careful with negatives as, if you ignore them, they can completely change the intended meaning.

4

5   Read this description of Marc's school.

> Mon collège est assez grand et il y a mille cinq cents élèves et plus de cent cinquante profs. Ma matière préférée, c'est le dessin et je m'entends très bien avec mon professeur. Par contre, je n'aime pas l'espagnol car je trouve ça barbant et inutile. Les cours commencent à huit heures et demie et je dois me lever tôt parce que je vais au collège en car. Je déteste ça. Le règlement n'est pas strict et j'ai plein de copains, alors ça va en général.

Answer the following questions **in English**.

Example: How many pupils go to Marc's school?   1500

> Be careful with larger numbers. It will pay to revise them.

5   **(a)**   What is his favourite subject?

Art ✓

(1 mark)

5   **(b)**   Why does he dislike Spanish? Give **two** reasons.

It is boring ✓ and useless. ✓

(2 marks)

5   **(c)**   When do his lessons start?

At 8:30. ✓

(1 mark)

5   **(d)**   How does he get to school?

He goes by coach. ✓

(1 mark)

5   **(e)**   Give **two** reasons why he thinks school is OK overall.

The rules are not strict ✓ and he has lots of friends. ✓

(2 marks)

5

6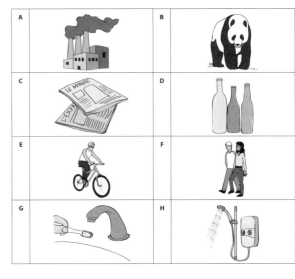

Read the following statements about the environment and match each one to the correct picture.

Write the correct letter in each box.

> Remember that sometimes recognising just one word in a sentence might allow you to come up with the correct answer.

Example: Je prends toujours une douche.   H

6   **(a)**   Je vais partout à pied.   F ✓   *(1 mark)*

6   **(b)**   Je me brosse les dents avec le robinet fermé.   G ✓   *(1 mark)*

6   **(c)**   Je recycle le verre.   D ✓   *(1 mark)*

6   **(d)**   Je déteste la pollution causée par les usines.   A ✓   *(1 mark)*

6

7   Read this email from Simon.

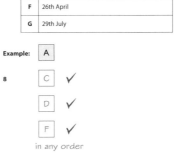

> Mail
> Fichier   Édition   Affichage   Composer   Envoyer   Aide
>
> Je suis très sportif. Je fais du judo trois fois par semaine et je nage tous les samedis. J'aime bien les sports d'équipe. Je joue au volley dans un club mais je ne joue plus au rugby car l'année dernière, je me suis cassé le bras pendant que j'y jouais et maintenant, je pense que c'est un sport assez dangereux. En hiver, mon frère fait du ski mais ce n'est pas mon truc. Je voudrais bien essayer le VTT un de ces jours. Mon père joue souvent au golf parce qu'il pense que c'est un bon moyen de rester en forme. Ma mère ne fait pas de sport mais elle aime regarder le tennis à la télé de temps en temps.

Decide which **four** of the following sentences are true.

Write the correct letter in each box.

A	Simon is very sporty.
B	Simon does judo twice a week.
C	Simon goes swimming once a week.
D	Simon does not play volleyball.
E	Simon used to play rugby.
F	Simon thinks that rugby is dangerous.
G	Simon goes skiing in winter.
H	Simon would like to go mountain biking.
I	Simon's brother likes golf.
J	Simon's mum plays tennis from time to time.

> Take care to read the whole passage in order to find the answers. A different person might have a different view about sports, for example. Here the father is also mentioned so do not confuse his activities or likes and dislikes with those of Simon.

Example: A

7   C ✓
E ✓
F ✓
H ✓

(4 marks)

in any order

7

8   Look at the dates of these events.

| Il y aura un festival de musique le onze juin. |
| Le concert de musique classique, c'est le vingt-six avril. |
| La fête, c'est le vingt-huit juillet. |
| Les cours de danse classique commenceront le dix-neuf juillet. |
| Rendez-vous au restaurant le quinze juin à huit heures. |
| Le nouveau cinéma ouvre le seize août. |

Which of the following dates are mentioned?

Write the correct **three** letters in the boxes.

A	11th June
B	11th July
C	16th August
D	19th July
E	28th April
F	26th April
G	29th July

> Remember to listen to the number in its entirety. Vingt-deux is 22, not 20 or 2.

Example: A

8   C ✓
D ✓
F ✓

(3 marks)

in any order

TOTAL FOR PAPER IS 35 MARKS

8

1   Sophie is talking about her friends.

How does she describe them?

A	tall
B	small
C	medium height
D	blond hair
E	black hair
F	thin
G	green eyes
H	blue eyes

> Listen for any familiar words first before trying to eliminate answers and having a sensible, informed guess as a last resort.

Listen and write the correct letter in each box.

Example: Louis   F

1   **(a)**   Romain   E ✓   *(1 mark)*

1   **(b)**   Raphaël   A ✓   *(1 mark)*

1   **(c)**   Maya   H ✓   *(1 mark)*

1   **(d)**   Soraya   B ✓   *(1 mark)*

9

2   Listen to these young people talking about their hobbies.
What does each person do?
Write the correct letter in each box.

A		B	
C		D	
E		F	
G		H	
I			Remember that the idea of liking is not important in any of these sentences, it will be much more important to listen for the activities.

Example: Paul   C

2   **(a)**   Léo   H ✓   *(1 mark)*

2   **(b)**   Lisa   I ✓   *(1 mark)*

2   **(c)**   Julie   D ✓   *(1 mark)*

2   **(d)**   Michel   F ✓   *(1 mark)*

2   **(e)**   Ramona   A ✓   *(1 mark)*

10

3   Listen to Bastien talking about his breakfast.

Answer the questions **in English**.

Example: When does he have breakfast?   7am

3   **(a)**   What does he usually drink?

> Listen for any familiar words first before trying to eliminate answers and having a sensible, informed guess as a last resort.

coffee ✓

(1 mark)

3   **(b)**   What does he usually eat?

bread ✓

jam ✓

(2 marks)

3   **(c)**   What does he eat when he is in a hurry?

apple ✓

(1 mark)

3   **(d)**   What does he have for breakfast at the weekend?

cereal ✓

hot chocolate ✓

(2 marks)

11

4   Listen to these young people talking about where they live.

Write the correct letter in each box.

A	A small town in the south of France.
B	A large town in the south of France.
C	A large town in the west of France.
D	A small town in the east of France.
E	A fishing port.
F	A small town by the sea.
G	A ski resort.
H	An industrial town in the north of France.
I	A small village in the mountains.

> Remember that *ville* and *village* are quite close in French but have different meanings. Adjectives of size will also be very important here.

Example: H

4   **(a)**   I ✓   *(1 mark)*

4   **(b)**   C ✓   *(1 mark)*

4   **(c)**   F ✓   *(1 mark)*

4   **(d)**   A ✓   *(1 mark)*

4   **(e)**   G ✓   *(1 mark)*

12

5   Listen to Élise talking about her school.

What are her opinions about the following?

Write **P** (positive), **N** (negative) or
P/N (positive and negative) in each box.

Example: Sport at school   N

5   **(a)**   School rules   P   ✓

> For positive and negative, there will sometimes be a contradicting connective such as *mais* (but) or *pourtant* (however).

(1 mark)

5   **(b)**   Maths   N   ✓   *(1 mark)*

5   **(c)**   The canteen   P   ✓   *(1 mark)*

5   **(d)**   The teachers   P/N   ✓   *(1 mark)*

5   **(e)**   The classrooms   N   ✓   *(1 mark)*

13

6   Listen to Axel talking about his holidays.

Complete the sentences by choosing the correct letter.

Write the correct letter in each box.

> Try to filter out any irrelevant material which does not help to guide you to the correct response, such as adjectives or adverbs.

Example: Axel usually goes to …

   A Italy   **B** Spain   **C** England   B

6   **(a)**   He normally travels by …

   A car   **B** plane   **C** boat   A   ✓   *(1 mark)*

6   **(b)**   Last year he went to …

   A Africa   **B** Wales   **C** Germany   B   ✓   *(1 mark)*

6   **(c)**   He found the staff at his hotel …

   A polite   **B** rude   **C** lazy   C   ✓   *(1 mark)*

6   **(d)**   Next year he is planning to …

   A visit his cousin   **B** go camping   **C** stay in France   A   ✓   *(1 mark)*

6   **(e)**   He hopes to …

   A sunbathe   **B** take long walks   **C** go fishing   B   ✓   *(1 mark)*

14

7   Listen to these people talking about ways to combat stress.

What does each person do?

Write the correct letter in each box.

A	Watch TV
B	Go to bed
C	Eat chocolate
D	Have a bath
E	Chat to friends
F	Talk to family
G	Have a hot drink
H	Take some exercise
I	Read
J	Listen to music

> Don't allow yourself to be distracted by what other people, such as friends, do or say they do. Focus on the person concerned each time.

Example: A

7   **(a)**   I   ✓   *(1 mark)*

7   **(b)**   B   ✓   *(1 mark)*

7   **(c)**   G   ✓   *(1 mark)*

7   **(d)**   E   ✓   *(1 mark)*

7   **(e)**   J   ✓   *(1 mark)*

TOTAL FOR PAPER IS 35 MARKS

15

1 Here are some types of TV programme.

A	un film de science-fiction
B	une émission de sport
C	un documentaire
D	une émission de télé-réalité
E	un dessin animé
F	une émission de musique pop
G	un feuilleton

Cognates are words which are the same in both English and French. Near cognates can also help you to work out the meaning of words.

Which programme would each of the following select?

Write the correct letter in each box.

Example: Marc likes football.   **B**

1 **(a)**   Lily likes cartoons.   E ✓   *(1 mark)*

1 **(b)**   Aimée likes documentaries.   C ✓   *(1 mark)*

1 **(c)**   Samy likes reality TV programmes.   D ✓   *(1 mark)*

1 **(d)**   Rémy likes soap operas.   G ✓   *(1 mark)*

2

A	Maths		B	Geography	
C	ICT		D	DT	
E	PE		F	Chemistry	
G	Drama				

What is each person's favourite subject?

Write the correct letter in each box.

Example: Je préfère les maths.   **A**

2 **(a)**   Moi, j'aime mieux l'informatique.   C ✓   *(1 mark)*

2 **(b)**   Ma matière préférée, c'est la chimie.   F ✓   *(1 mark)*

2 **(c)**   J'adore le théâtre.   G ✓   *(1 mark)*

2 **(d)**   Je préfère la technologie.   D ✓   *(1 mark)*

Cognates are words which are the same in both English and French. Near cognates can also help you to work out the meaning of words. Remember that you might also like to eliminate answers so if you know a word in the options given and do not see it, this might mean that it is not used anywhere as an answer and this could help you to cut down the number of possible answers left.

---

3 Read this email about Élodie's family.

Dans ma famille, il y a six personnes. Je n'ai pas de sœurs mais j'ai deux frères cadets. J'ai un frère aîné, Michel, qui adore les ordinateurs mais mes frères cadets, Julien et Mathis, préfèrent faire de l'équitation. Mon passetemps préféré, c'est dessiner. Je m'entends bien avec mes parents car ils sont compréhensifs. Mon père est facteur et ma mère travaille dans une banque.

Answer the following questions.

Write the correct letter in each box.

Look for key words to identify the person involved in the question and also try to look for other words that could express how old someone might be.

Example: How many people are there in Élodie's family?

   A 4   B 5   C 6   **C**

3 **(a)**   How many older brothers does she have?

   A 0   B 1   C 2   B ✓ *(1 mark)*

3 **(b)**   Why does she get on well with her parents?

   A They are generous.   B They are not strict.   C They are understanding.   C ✓ *(1 mark)*

3 **(c)**   What is her father's job?

   A a postman   B a factory worker   C a bank clerk   A ✓ *(1 mark)*

3 **(d)**   What does Michel like?

   A swimming   B computers   C cycling   B ✓ *(1 mark)*

3 **(e)**   What does Julien like?

   A swimming   B horse riding   C fishing   B ✓ *(1 mark)*

---

4 Read the following programme for a school exchange.

A	lundi	Excursion au parc d'attractions
B	mardi	Après-midi au centre commercial
C	mercredi	Visite du musée des voitures
D	jeudi	Journée avec les familles d'accueil
E	vendredi	Excursion au château fort
F	samedi	Journée au centre sportif municipal
G	dimanche	Fête à l'hôtel de ville

Find the correct day for these activities.

Write the correct letter in each box.

Remember that sometimes recognising just one word in a sentence might allow you to come up with the correct answer.

Example: Sporting activities   **F**

4 **(a)**   Visit to a castle   E ✓   *(1 mark)*

4 **(b)**   Party in the town hall   G ✓   *(1 mark)*

4 **(c)**   Shopping   B ✓   *(1 mark)*

4 **(d)**   Looking at vintage cars   C ✓   *(1 mark)*

5 Read these opinions about jobs.

For each one give an advantage and a disadvantage.

> Look for key adjectives, both positive and negative.

Write the answers **in English** in each box.

> Je pense que travailler comme vendeur est facile, mais d'un autre côté, c'est ennuyeux.

Example:

Job	Advantage	Disadvantage
Shop assistant	Easy	Boring

1 Travailler comme infirmière, c'est bien, car on aide les autres, mais je sais aussi que les heures de travail sont très longues.

2 Il y a des avantages et des inconvénients à être professeur parce qu'on est bien payé mais les élèves peuvent être difficiles.

3 Je voudrais être fermier car j'adore le travail en plein air, mais j'ai peur des vaches.

Job			Advantage	Disadvantage
5	**(a)**	Nurse	Help others ✓	Long hours ✓
5	**(b)**	Teacher	Well paid ✓	Pupils (can be) difficult ✓
5	**(c)**	Farmer	Likes fresh air ✓	Frightened of cows ✓

(6 marks)

20

---

6 Read this email from Anaïs.

Bolte de réception

Salut! C'est moi, Anaïs. Tu m'as demandé de t'écrire au sujet de la santé. Je fais attention à ce que je mange. Par exemple, j'essaie de ne pas manger de bonbons et j'évite aussi les matières grasses. En plus, je bois beaucoup d'eau et je ne consomme jamais d'alcool. Il y a quelques années, j'ai essayé une cigarette, mais je ne fume pas car c'est mauvais pour la santé. Je ne suis pas sportive et je ne fais pas d'exercice physique sauf aux cours d'EPS au collège. Cependant, à l'avenir, je vais aller plus souvent à la piscine et je jouerai au squash avec mon frère.

Decide if the following sentences are **T** (true), **F** (false) or **?** (not mentioned).

> Remember negatives like *jamais* often provide key items of information for answers.

Example: Anaïs was asked to write about health. | T |

6 **(a)** Anaïs eats a lot of sweets. | F | ✓   *(1 mark)*

6 **(b)** She is a vegetarian. | ? | ✓   *(1 mark)*

6 **(c)** She drinks alcohol from time to time. | F | ✓   *(1 mark)*

6 **(d)** She tried smoking. | T | ✓   *(1 mark)*

6 **(e)** She does no sports except PE at school. | T | ✓   *(1 mark)*

6 **(f)** She is planning to do more swimming. | T | ✓   *(1 mark)*

21

---

7 Read what these three young people do to celebrate their birthdays.

 Charlotte: D'habitude, pour fêter mon anniversaire, mes parents organisent une fête chez nous. Tous mes copains sont invités et on danse, on écoute de la musique et on mange bien. L'année dernière, j'ai décidé de passer la journée au parc d'attractions avec ma meilleure copine et c'était vraiment génial.

 Mathilde: Moi, je n'aime pas les fêtes, alors normalement, je sors en ville avec quelques copains et on dîne ensemble dans un restaurant chinois. L'année prochaine, j'aurai dix-huit ans et mes parents vont organiser une soirée musicale avec des feux d'artifice. J'attends ça avec impatience!

 Noémie: Je viens d'avoir dix-huit ans et pour mon anniversaire, j'ai passé la journée au bord de la mer avec ma famille. Ma sœur et moi avons fait de la planche à voile et c'était très amusant. L'année prochaine, mes parents vont louer une salle dans un hôtel de luxe et nous fêterons l'événement avec plein d'amis.

Answer the following questions.

Write **C** (Charlotte), **M** (Mathilde) or **N** (Noémie) in each box.

Example: Who usually has a party for her birthday? | C |

7 **(a)** Who does not like parties? | M | ✓   *(1 mark)*

7 **(b)** Who has just turned 18? | N | ✓   *(1 mark)*

7 **(c)** Who went windsurfing on her birthday? | N | ✓   *(1 mark)*

7 **(d)** Who went out with her best friend last year? | C | ✓   *(1 mark)*

7 **(e)** Who is planning to have fireworks as part of next year's celebration? | M | ✓   *(1 mark)*

7 **(f)** Who usually spends her birthday at home? | C | ✓   *(1 mark)*

> Take care with idioms such as the use of *venir de+* infinitive, which means to have just done something but could look like a present or even a future tense, when in essence it sites the action in the past.

TOTAL FOR PAPER IS 35 MARKS

22

1 Where do these people like to go at the weekend?

Write the correct letter in each box.

Concentrate solely on the places or activities here.

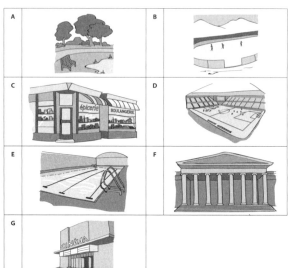

A		B	
C		D	
E		F	
G			

Example: | G |

1 **(a)** | C | ✓ (1 mark)

1 **(b)** | E | ✓ (1 mark)

1 **(c)** | D | ✓ (1 mark)

1 **(d)** | B | ✓ (1 mark)

23

2 Lise is talking about her work experience.

Which things does she mention?

Write the correct letter in each box.

A	her boss
B	her colleagues
C	her journey to work
D	what she did at lunchtime
E	the starting and finishing times
F	what she ate for lunch
G	her clothes
H	her plans for the future
I	her opinion of the work experience
J	her daily tasks

Remember that the question does not require you to understand opinions or reasons, so stay focused on listening for the key word in the options available.

Example: | B |

2 | A | ✓

| C | ✓

| G | ✓

| I | ✓

| J | ✓ (5 marks)

in any order

24

3 Listen to Alicia talking about her friends.

Write the correct letter in each box.

A	dynamic
B	good at sport
C	generous
D	shy
E	hard-working
F	cool
G	kind
H	clever
I	talkative

Adjectives will be vitally important to listen for here.

Example: Pauline | A |

3 **(a)** Lucille | D | ✓ (1 mark)

3 **(b)** Anna | H | ✓ (1 mark)

3 **(c)** Benjamin | B | ✓ (1 mark)

3 **(d)** Mélissa | I | ✓ (1 mark)

3 **(e)** Abdi | E | ✓ (1 mark)

25

4 Listen to Tristan talking about his likes and dislikes.

Which **five** things are mentioned?

Write the correct letter in each box.

A	his favourite colour
B	games consoles
C	going to the theatre
D	skiing
E	books
F	football
G	spiders
H	roller skating
I	eating out

Remember that the question does not require you to understand opinions or reasons, so stay focused on listening for the key word in the options available.

Example: | A |

4 | B | ✓

| C | ✓

| E | ✓

| H | ✓

| I | ✓ (5 marks)

in any order

26

5   Listen to Sarah talking about her school.

Which **four** statements are true?

Write the correct letter in each box.

A	Sarah loves IT.
B	She finds chemistry interesting.
C	She likes her maths teacher.
D	Her favourite subject is art.
E	She used to like English.
F	She has French four times a week.
G	She usually goes home for lunch.
H	She thinks she has too many French lessons.
I	She has changed her opinion about history.

> Pay special attention to negatives, particularly *ne … plus* (no longer) and tenses.

Example: A

5   D ✓

E ✓

G ✓

H ✓   *(4 marks)*

in any order

27

---

6   Listen to these young people talking about relationships.

Fill in the gaps **in English**.

Example: Camille would like to meet someone with **brown eyes** .

6   **(a)**   Lilou would like to meet a boy who is ____ tall ✓ ____ and has ____ blond ✓ ____ hair.
                                                              (2 marks)

6   **(b)**   Léon wants to meet a girl who is ____ funny ✓ ____ but he thinks that her ____ appearance ✓ ____ is not important.
                                                              (2 marks)

6   **(c)**   Aurélie would like to meet someone who is ____ serious ✓ ____ but does not like people who

are ____ selfish ✓ ____.   *(2 marks)*

> Make sure that the word you put into the spaces allows the sentence to make sense in English. If it does not, then it is almost certainly the wrong answer.

28

---

7   What job does each person want to do?

Write the correct letter in each box.

A	vet
B	doctor
C	nurse
D	shop assistant
E	mechanic
F	policeman
G	hairdresser
H	teacher
I	gardener
J	engineer
K	IT worker

> Pay attention to the task. You are listening for jobs so don't allow yourself to be put off by other information given.

Example: J

7   **(a)**   K ✓   *(1 mark)*

7   **(b)**   G ✓   *(1 mark)*

7   **(c)**   C ✓   *(1 mark)*

7   **(d)**   B ✓   *(1 mark)*

7   **(e)**   D ✓   *(1 mark)*

7   **(f)**   I ✓   *(1 mark)*

TOTAL FOR PAPER IS 35 MARKS

29

1 Read this account of Martin's holiday.

> J'aime aller en vacances à la montagne car l'air est pur. Cependant, la semaine dernière, j'ai passé mes vacances au bord de la mer en Italie avec ma famille. J'adore partir en vacances avec mes parents car ils payent tout mais mon petit frère m'énerve, surtout en vacances.
>
> Notre hôtel était situé tout près de la plage, ce qui m'a vraiment plu. J'ai dû partager ma chambre avec mon frère ce qui m'a déplu car je ne m'entends pas bien avec lui. Mais heureusement, la chambre était grande et bien équipée.
>
> Il y avait un restaurant au sous-sol où on a mangé chaque soir. Les repas étaient formidables pour la plupart, sauf le dernier soir quand on nous a servi du poisson trop épicé. Je n'ai pas du tout aimé ça!
>
> À mon avis, la piscine de l'hôtel n'était pas propre et l'eau était froide, alors j'ai préféré me baigner dans la mer. Un jour, nous avons décidé de visiter un château dans la région. Mes parents l'ont trouvé très intéressant mais moi, je l'ai trouvé barbant.
>
> Il n'y a pas eu de problème pendant le vol de retour et nous sommes arrivés chez nous à l'heure.

What is Martin's opinion of the following?

Write **P** (positive), **N** (negative) or **P/N** (positive and negative) in each box.

Example	Mountain holidays	**P**		
1 **(a)**	Family holidays	P/N	✓	(1 mark)
1 **(b)**	The location of the hotel	P	✓	(1 mark)
1 **(c)**	His room	P/N	✓	(1 mark)
1 **(d)**	The meals in the restaurant	P/N	✓	(1 mark)
1 **(e)**	The hotel pool	N	✓	(1 mark)
1 **(f)**	The castle	N	✓	(1 mark)
1 **(g)**	The return journey	P	✓	(1 mark)

> Think of as many different ways as you can to express a positive and negative opinion in French before you consider a question like this. That might help you discover rarer versions of opinions (e.g. *ça me plaît/déplaît*).

2 Read Enzo's comments about sports.

> Je suis assez actif et je sais qu'il faut faire du sport afin de rester en forme. Mon frère n'est pas sportif et il n'aime pas le sport. Il préfère rester devant son ordinateur! En hiver, je dois jouer au foot et au rugby au collège mais je n'aime pas ça car les sports d'équipe sont difficiles pour moi. Mon sport préféré, c'est le VTT mais j'aime aussi faire de la natation.
>
> Quand j'étais plus jeune, je jouais au tennis deux fois par semaine mais je n'y joue plus. Ma sœur joue bien et elle s'entraîne tous les jeudis. Mon père joue au golf de temps en temps et il fait de la planche à voile en été. Le seul exercice physique que fait ma mère, c'est du jogging.
>
> À l'avenir, j'ai l'intention de faire plus de sport. Je pense que je vais essayer de faire de la voile et aussi du ski nautique.

Complete the answers by selecting the correct letter.

> Be careful with hidden negatives like *ne … que* (only) which do not have a full negative force.

Example:	Enzo knows that …	**A** he is very sporty	**B** he should do sport to keep fit	**C** he is very fit	**B**		
2 **(a)**	His brother …	**A** is very active	**B** likes spending time on his computer	**C** loves sport	B	✓	(1 mark)
2 **(b)**	In winter Enzo …	**A** plays no sport	**B** watches rugby and football	**C** plays sport at school	C	✓	(1 mark)
2 **(c)**	He dislikes team sports because …	**A** he finds them difficult	**B** he finds them boring	**C** he hates playing against his friends	A	✓	(1 mark)
2 **(d)**	His favourite sport is …	**A** swimming	**B** mountain biking	**C** tennis	B	✓	(1 mark)
2 **(e)**	He used to …	**A** go training on Thursdays	**B** go swimming regularly	**C** play tennis twice a week	C	✓	(1 mark)
2 **(f)**	His father …	**A** goes jogging	**B** plays golf every day	**C** goes windsurfing in summer	C	✓	(1 mark)
2 **(q)**	In the future Enzo …	**A** would like to try sailing	**B** wants to do more skiing	**C** plans to do less sport	A	✓	(1 mark)

3 Match the two halves of each sentence so that they make sense.

Write the correct letter in each box.

(a)	Moi, je voudrais travailler …	**A**	très dur.
(b)	L'année dernière, j'ai fait mon stage …	**B**	comme pompier.
(c)	Mon père travaille …	**C**	il faut trouver un emploi bien payé.
(d)	Mes parents pensent qu' …	**D**	de trouver un petit job.
(e)	Je n'ai …	**E**	dans un magasin de musique.
(f)	J'ai un petit job qui …	**F**	aucune envie d'être professeur.
(g)	Mon copain vient …	**G**	me plaît.

Example: (a)   Moi, je voudrais travailler …   **B**

3 **(b)**	L'année dernière, j'ai fait mon stage …	E	✓	(1 mark)
3 **(c)**	Mon père travaille …	A	✓	(1 mark)
3 **(d)**	Mes parents pensent qu' …	C	✓	(1 mark)
3 **(e)**	Je n'ai …	F	✓	(1 mark)
3 **(f)**	J'ai un petit job qui …	G	✓	(1 mark)
3 **(g)**	Mon copain vient …	D	✓	(1 mark)

> A difficult grammar-based question like this means that you have to be sure that what you are left with makes total sense in French. For example, *je n'ai* … suggests a negative, but at first glance, there are none. However, negatives are not just *ne … pas*!

4 Read Margot's email about her education.

> **Mail**
> Fichier Édition Affichage Composer Envoyer Aide
>
> Salut!
> Tu m'as demandé de te parler un peu de ma vie scolaire.
> Quand j'étais petite, j'allais à une école primaire qui était tout près de ma maison. À mon avis, c'était tout à fait agréable car les instituteurs étaient enthousiastes et je n'avais pas de devoirs. Je m'intéressais aux cours et je m'amusais bien, surtout pendant les cours de dessin et de lecture.
> À l'âge de onze ans, je suis allée à un grand collège qui me semblait énorme. J'étais un peu malheureuse car la plupart de mes amis proches sont allés ailleurs et je me sentais isolée. J'ai trouvé les cours assez durs mais j'ai réussi à trouver de bons copains et j'ai eu de bons résultats, surtout en langues et en chimie. Mes profs étaient plus sévères que mes anciens instituteurs, mais je m'entendais bien avec mon prof d'EPS.
> Margot

Answer the questions **in English**.

Example: Where was Margot's primary school? **Near her house.**

4 **(a)** Why do you think Margot was happy at primary school? Give **two** details apart from lessons.

Teachers enthusiastic ✓ got no homework ✓

(2 marks)

4 **(b)** Which of her lessons did she particularly like?

art ✓ reading ✓

(2 marks)

4 **(c)** Why did she feel unhappy when she started secondary school? Give **two** details.

any two from:
felt alone ✓ friends had gone to other schools ✓ it was an enormous place ✓ lessons hard ✓

(2 marks)

4 **(d)** What did she finally manage to do? Give **two** details.

any two from:
make good friends ✓ excel in chemistry ✓ and in languages ✓

(2 marks)

4 **(e)** Why could you argue that she did not feel totally against her teachers?

got on well with PE teacher ✓

(1 mark)

> At this level a degree of inference is needed to get the correct answers, so make sure that you read the whole passage, looking for clues which might give you a hint as to what is needed. Be especially careful when your opinion is requested as this will be an inference question.

5   Read Rakim's account of life in Africa.

> J'habite au Sénégal, en Afrique, depuis ma naissance. Comme dans beaucoup de pays, il y a de gros problèmes. Le chômage et la faim sont les pires. Heureusement, mon père a un emploi, donc on a assez à manger, mais j'ai peur de ne pas pouvoir trouver de travail ici plus tard.
>
> À cause de la sécheresse, on ne peut pas cultiver suffisamment de nourriture, alors on a besoin de l'aide des pays riches comme la France. Puisque je suis doué en langues, j'espère aller vivre à l'étranger à l'avenir, soit en Allemagne, soit en Belgique. Si je réussis à trouver un emploi, j'enverrai de l'argent à ma famille, comme ça tout le monde pourra déménager aussi.
>
> Mon cousin vient de partir pour aller vivre en France où il est footballeur professionnel et à mon avis, il a de la chance!

Which **five** statements are true according to the text?

Write the correct letters in each box.

A	Rakim lives in Senegal.	B	Rakim has just moved to France.
C	Unemployment is a serious problem in Senegal.	D	Rakim's father is unemployed.
E	Rakim is worried about his own future.	F	It doesn't rain much in Rakim's area of Senegal.
G	Rakim plans to learn French in the future.	H	Rakim has sent money to his family.
I	He hopes to live abroad in the future.	J	His family has recently moved house.
K	Rakim thinks his cousin is lucky.		

Example: A

5   C ✓

 E ✓

F ✓

 I ✓

K ✓

in any order

> Take care to recognise tenses with appropriate vocabulary, as there may be answers which are correct at first glance, until you ensure that you have the correct tense.

(5 marks)

34

---

6   Read these comments about relationships.

 Sarah: J'aimerais me marier un jour mais je sais que je voudrais aller à l'université avant. J'ai un petit ami depuis trois ans mais je ne sais pas si nous serons ensemble plus tard. Quant aux enfants, j'en voudrais deux, un garçon et une fille.

 Delphine: Je suis contre le mariage parce que je voudrais rester indépendante. Néanmoins, je crois que j'aurai un compagnon un jour et mon compagnon idéal aurait les mêmes goûts et les mêmes centres d'intérêt que moi. Cependant, je n'aimerais pas avoir d'enfants.

 Juliette: Moi, je ne sais pas si je me marierai à l'avenir mais je suis sûre que j'aimerais avoir plusieurs enfants. Mes parents sont divorcés et quand j'étais jeune, ils se sont beaucoup disputés, ce qui m'énervait énormément. J'étais souvent triste à cause de leurs disputes. Je viens de rencontrer un garçon qui me plaît, mais je ne pense pas qu'on restera ensemble.

Answer the following questions.

Write **S** (Sarah), **D** (Delphine) or **J** (Juliette) in each box.

Example:		Who wants to get married in the future?	S		
6	**(a)**	Who does not want children?	D	✓	(1 mark)
6	**(b)**	Who has been in a steady relationship for some time?	S	✓	(1 mark)
6	**(c)**	Who wants an education before marrying?	S	✓	(1 mark)
6	**(d)**	Who has just met a boy she likes?	J	✓	(1 mark)
6	**(e)**	Who was unhappy when she was younger?	J	✓	(1 mark)
6	**(f)**	Who would like to find someone who shares her tastes?	D	✓	(1 mark)

> Looking for specific detail in questions of this nature will often lead you past a distracter, to the correct answer. Different people may say very similar things on the same topic, so precision will be needed to get the correct answer.

TOTAL FOR PAPER IS 40 MARKS

35

1   Listen to these young people talking about where they live.

For each person give a positive and negative of where they live.

Answer the questions **in English**.

	☺	☹
Example:	Near school	No ice rink
1 (a)	lots of shops / can go shopping ✓	(too) noisy (in evening) ✓
1 (b)	quiet ✓	no buses / need a car ✓
1 (c)	historic monuments ✓	streets dirty ✓

(6 marks)

> Try to be specific in your answers. If, for example you are asked for a disadvantage and a specific noun and adjective are mentioned, just including one would not be sufficient to gain the mark.

---

2   Listen to these young people's opinions about TV programmes.

For each one write P (positive opinion), N (negative opinion) or P/N (positive and negative opinion) in each box.

Example: N

> Always listen through to the end of an utterance in questions like this in case there is evidence of positive and negative opinions. If you hear one, don't write P or N straight away.

2   (a)   N ✓   *(1 mark)*

2   (b)   P/N ✓   *(1 mark)*

2   (c)   P/N ✓   *(1 mark)*

2   (d)   P ✓   *(1 mark)*

---

3   Listen to the following people discussing their future plans.

Find the most suitable job in the list.

For each person, write the correct letter in each box.

A	doctor
B	hairdresser
C	mechanic
D	chef
E	police officer
F	secretary
G	shop assistant
H	farmer
I	greengrocer
J	postman

> The key issue here is the job, so filter out other details, but remember the place could have a bearing on the job and the actual French word for the job may not be present at this level.

Example: G

3   (a)   A ✓   *(1 mark)*

3   (b)   E ✓   *(1 mark)*

3   (c)   H ✓   *(1 mark)*

3   (d)   D ✓   *(1 mark)*

3   (e)   C ✓   *(1 mark)*

---

4   Listen to Clément and Safia talking about technology.

> Be careful in questions where there is a qualifier such as 'main'; you might very well hear other uses too but they will not be the correct answer.

Answer the questions.

Write the correct letter in each box.

Example: How old is Clément?

A   15   B   16   C   17   B

Part 1   Answer questions **4 (a)–4 (c)**.

4   (a)   What is the main reason Clément uses his mobile phone?

A   to text his friends   B   to let his parents know that he is running late   C   to take photos   A ✓   *(1 mark)*

4   (b)   How does he describe his new phone?

A   very small   B   the latest model   C   the best model   B ✓   *(1 mark)*

4   (c)   What does he plan to use his phone to do in the future?

A   listen to music   B   watch videos   C   get sports results   C ✓   *(1 mark)*

Part 2   Answer questions **4 (d)–4 (f)**.

4   (d)   Why does Safia prefer to use a word processor?

A   she has poor handwriting   B   it's easier   C   she thinks it's more formal   A ✓   *(1 mark)*

4   (e)   What has happened as a result of Safia using chatrooms?

A   she has done less sport   B   she has had her identity stolen   C   she has made friends   C ✓   *(1 mark)*

4   (f)   How often does she check her emails?

A   once an hour   B   once a day   C   every 10 minutes   B ✓   *(1 mark)*

5   Listen to Almeira talking about her life.

Answer the questions **in English**.

> Don't be put off by extra verbs like *décide de* or *commencer à* as they only serve to introduce the main, more important verb.

Example: Where does Almeira live? Togo

Part 1   Answer questions **5 (a)** and **5 (b).**

5   **(a)**   Which **two** problems does Almeira mention about Togo?

unemployment ....✓...

floods....✓...

(2 marks)

5   **(b)**   Why is life now a little easier for Almeira's family?

Her mother has got a job as a cleaner.   ✓

(1 mark)

Part 2   Answer questions **5 (c)** and **5 (d).**

5   **(c)**   Which **two** industries used to flourish in Lomé?

fishing....✓..

clothing....✓..

(2 marks)

5   **(d)**   What has Almeira's brother decided to do?

try to find work   ✓

gone to France   ✓

(2 marks)

Part 3   Answer questions **5 (e)** and **5 (f).**

5   **(e)**   What makes Almeira pessimistic for her future?

has no qualifications   ✓

(1 mark)

5   **(f)**   Which **two** environmental problems does she mention?

deforestation   ✓

animals becoming extinct   ✓

(2 marks)

40

6   Listen to Jasmine talking about holidays.

A	Jasmine prefers active holidays.	B	Her sister loves sunbathing.
C	Her brother was sick on holiday last year.	D	Jasmine is afraid of flying.
E	Jasmine would like to visit America.	F	Her dad has never been abroad.
G	Her mum loves museums.	H	Jasmine has never been skiing.
I	Her sister likes swimming.	J	Jasmine hates camping.
K	Her mum has been to Switzerland.	L	Jasmine prefers holidays with friends.

Find the **five** correct statements according to the text.

Write the correct letter in each box.

> Tenses and subjects of verbs are vital in questions of this nature.

Example: | A |

6

| C | ✓

| G | ✓

| I | ✓

| B | ✓

| F | ✓

(5 marks)

in any order

41

7   Listen to Paul talking about pocket money.

A	tidy his room
B	go shopping for his grandfather
C	help out at a youth club
D	mow the lawn
E	walk the neighbour's dog
F	look after the neighbour's cats
G	get good marks at school
H	buy computer games
I	buy clothes
J	go out with friends

> As the task just deals with things mentioned, there is no need to listen particularly for tenses or likes/dislikes here.

Which **four** things has Paul done?

Write the correct letter in each box.

Example: | A |

7

| D | ✓

| G | ✓

| F | ✓

| J | ✓

(4 marks)

in any order

TOTAL FOR PAPER IS 40 MARKS

42

1   Read Armand's comments about where he lives.

J'habite dans un HLM dans la banlieue de Paris. C'est un quartier qui était chic avant mais maintenant, ce n'est plus très populaire. Comme dans toutes les grandes villes, il y a des problèmes environnementaux comme la pollution car il y a plein de camions qui font des livraisons et les embouteillages sont nombreux, surtout aux heures de pointe.

Bien sûr, il y a des zones piétonnes, mais je pense qu'il faut créer plus d'espaces verts. En plus, je pense qu'il faudrait obliger les automobilistes à payer s'ils veulent entrer dans le centre-ville, comme ça on réduirait non seulement le nombre de véhicules en ville mais aussi les gaz d'échappement.

For each sentence write **T** (true), **F** (false) or **?** (not mentioned) in each box.

Example: Armand lives in a house.   **F**

1   **(a)**   He lives in a smart area of Paris.   F ✓   *(1 mark)*

1   **(b)**   He thinks that Paris has the same problems as other cities.   T ✓   *(1 mark)*

1   **(c)**   He thinks that lorries are partly to blame for pollution.   T ✓   *(1 mark)*

1   **(d)**   He thinks that Paris is an affluent place.   ? ✓   *(1 mark)*

1   **(e)**   There are pedestrian zones in Paris.   T ✓   *(1 mark)*

1   **(f)**   He thinks there should be more cycle paths.   ? ✓   *(1 mark)*

1   **(g)**   He believes that motorists should pay to enter the city.   T ✓   *(1 mark)*

> Tenses are important once again. Remember that the conditional translates the English 'would'.

43

---

2   Read these job adverts.

A	Nous cherchons un vendeur pour notre magasin de vêtements au centre-ville. Salaire: 12 euros par heure. Weekends de 9h à 17h.
B	On cherche serveur/serveuse pour un restaurant intime et chaleureux, situé près de la gare. Travail tous les jours sauf le vendredi. Pourboires partagés entre le personnel.
C	Propriétaire d'une nouvelle entreprise commerciale cherche secrétaire. Expérience essentielle. Salaire à négocier. Lundi–vendredi.
D	On cherche quelqu'un pour nettoyer le centre sportif tous les soirs de 20h à 22h sauf le dimanche. Salaire: dix euros par heure.
E	Supermarché Pascal cherche boulanger, plus de dix-huit ans. Travail tous les matins de 5h à 8h. 7 euros par heure.

Which advert mentions the following?

Write the correct letter in the box.

> In questions where you are selecting from a number of options, words like *sauf* (except) become vital as they have the power to drastically alter the meaning of a sentence.

Example: supermarket work   E

2   **(a)**   working as a cleaner   D ✓   *(1 mark)*

2   **(b)**   working every day   E ✓   *(1 mark)*

2   **(c)**   working near the station   B ✓   *(1 mark)*

2   **(d)**   selling clothes   A ✓   *(1 mark)*

2   **(e)**   working as a baker   E ✓   *(1 mark)*

2   **(f)**   tips shared   B ✓   *(1 mark)*

2   **(g)**   salary to be decided   C ✓   *(1 mark)*

2   **(h)**   working for a new company   C ✓   *(1 mark)*

44

---

3   Read this article about Jean's lifestyle.

Je réussis à résister à presque toutes sortes de friandises mais j'adore le chocolat, même si je sais que c'est mauvais pour la santé. Tous les jours, je prends un petit déjeuner copieux car c'est important de bien manger le matin. Des fois, je suis pressé, mais je ne saute jamais ce repas essentiel. Par contre, je ne prends qu'un déjeuner léger, soit des framboises ou des prunes, soit des noix. Le soir, on mange toujours à table en famille mais j'essaie de limiter ma consommation de viande rouge.

J'ai plein de copains qui boivent de l'alcool mais moi, je n'en bois pas car avoir la forme, c'est important pour moi. J'évite les boissons gazeuses et je bois beaucoup d'eau parce que c'est bon pour la peau.

Answer the questions **in English**.

Example: What can Jean not resist eating?   *chocolate*

3   **(a)**   Why do you think that Jean's morning routine is healthy? Give **two** details.

He has a big breakfast ✓ and never skips breakfast. ✓

(2 marks)

3   **(b)**   What does he have for lunch? Name any **two** items.

Any two of raspberries, ✓ plums, ✓ nuts. ✓

(2 marks)

3   **(c)**   Why do you think that Jean's family has traditional values?

They eat together as a family at the table. ✓

(1 mark)

3   **(d)**   What type of food is Jean trying to limit?

red meat ✓

(1 mark)

3   **(e)**   What **two** types of drink does Jean avoid drinking?

alcohol ✓ and fizzy drinks ✓

(2 marks)

3   **(f)**   Why does he drink lots of water?

It is good for your skin. ✓

(1 mark)

> Apart from questions which require you to filter information and pick out the correct answer from irrelevant, extraneous material, you also need to answer inference questions where you are asked 'why?'. Rely on your ability to read between the lines and not simply to find a correct word or answer.

45

---

4   Read this letter.

Hier soir, je suis allée manger dans votre restaurant «Le Toulousain» avec ma famille. Nous étions très déçus car nous avons eu plusieurs problèmes. D'abord, mon père avait réservé une table pour sept heures trente, mais on a dû attendre un quart d'heure au bar avant de pouvoir dîner. Le service était lent et la serveuse n'était pas très polie. En plus, j'ai choisi du poulet rôti avec des haricots verts mais tout était froid! Il n'y avait plus de tarte aux pommes, ce qui a beaucoup embêté ma mère, et le café qu'on nous a servi était trop fort.

Je ne reviendrai pas.

Sandrine Dumoulin

Answer the questions.

Put the correct letter in each box.

Example: When did Sandrine go to the restaurant?

A   last week   B   last month   C   yesterday   C

4   **(a)**   How did the family feel at the end of the meal?

A   angry   B   disappointed   C   happy   B ✓   *(1 mark)*

4   **(b)**   When did they sit down to eat?

A   7:30   B   7:45   C   8:00   B ✓   *(1 mark)*

4   **(c)**   What did Sandrine say about the service?

A   it was acceptable   B   the waitress was polite   C   it was slow   C ✓   *(1 mark)*

4   **(d)**   What was wrong with her meal?

A   it was too spicy   B   it was not warm enough   C   it had the wrong vegetables   B ✓   *(1 mark)*

4   **(e)**   What annoyed her mother?

A   the dessert she wanted was unavailable   B   she was allergic to the apples   C   her tart tasted bad   A ✓   *(1 mark)*

4   **(f)**   What was wrong with the coffee?

A   it was cold when it arrived   B   there was no milk   C   it was too strong   C ✓   *(1 mark)*

> Questions at this level will sometimes ask you to interpret words you know that are a little more difficult than the obvious ones. For example, a time may not be explicitly mentioned but you may need to sort through other information to arrive at the correct answer. In addition, synonyms may help you find the correct solution at other times.

46

80

5 Read Marc's comments about smoking.

> Je ne fumerai jamais puisque je n'ai aucune envie de devenir accro au tabac. Avant, ma tante fumait mais elle a arrêté il y a six mois. Elle était souvent hors d'haleine mais maintenant, elle va mieux et elle vient de s'inscrire à une salle de gym. Je suis pour les campagnes anti-tabac en France parce que trop de jeunes fument, et selon un sondage récent, les Français commencent à fumer de plus en plus tôt.

Which of the following does he mention?

Write the correct letter in each box.

> Remember that some words or expressions may have several meanings, for example, *il y a* can be 'there is/are' or 'ago'.

A	His reason for never smoking
B	His uncle's problems with smoking
C	A family member's success story
D	His aunt's future plans to join a gym
E	Campaigns to stop French people smoking
F	His attempts to give up smoking
G	His support for anti-smoking programmes
H	At what age French people start smoking

Example: G

5   A ✓

C ✓

E ✓

H ✓

in any order   *(4 marks)*

6 Select the correct word from the table below to fill each gap.

Write the correct letter in each box.

A	vais
B	voudrais
C	ferai
D	devenir
E	aller
F	suis
G	épouser
H	aimerait
I	vont
J	voyager
K	payé
L	avoir

> This type of question is common at the higher tier and requires you to be accurate and precise in your understanding of French grammar. Remember that *d'* followed by a gap must be followed by a word starting with a vowel in French (a, e, i, o, u, y) or h.

Example: Je A continuer mes études au lycée l'année prochaine.

6 **(a)** Plus tard, dans la vie, je voudrais D informaticien. ✓   *(1 mark)*

6 **(b)** Après L fini mes études, je chercherai un emploi. ✓   *(1 mark)*

6 **(c)** Mon copain H aller à l'université. ✓   *(1 mark)*

6 **(d)** Je C le tour du monde en avion. ✓   *(1 mark)*

6 **(e)** Mon rêve est de trouver un emploi bien K , comme ça j'aurai assez d'argent. ✓   *(1 mark)*

6 **(f)** Ma sœur a l'intention d' G un homme riche, plus tard. ✓   *(1 mark)*

TOTAL FOR PAPER IS 40 MARKS

1 Listen to these young people talking about their leisure activities.

For each person, choose an answer from each box.

Write the letters in the correct boxes.

	Activities		Time
A	fishing	**(i)**	next Saturday
B	windsurfing	**(ii)**	last Sunday
C	shopping	**(iii)**	18h30
D	sailing	**(iv)**	8h30
E	chess	**(v)**	next month
F	ice skating	**(vi)**	16h30
G	swimming	**(vii)**	last week
H	horse riding	**(viii)**	16h45

	Activities	Time
Example:	E	iv
1 (a)	C ✓	i ✓
1 (b)	H ✓	vii ✓
1 (c)	B ✓	vi ✓
1 (d)	A ✓	v ✓

(8 marks)

> Again, take care with negatives which might distract. Listen for numbers with care and remember that the French often use the 24 hour clock.

49

2 Which special occasion is being discussed?

Write the correct letter in each box.

> If you do not know the French for the words in the box, try to listen for other associated clues to help.

A	Easter
B	New Year's Day
C	A birthday
D	All Saints' Day
E	New Year's Eve
F	Christmas Eve
G	Christmas Day
H	A wedding
I	A christening
J	An engagement

Example: F

2 (a) A ✓

2 (b) C ✓

2 (c) I ✓

2 (d) B ✓

2 (e) J ✓

(5 marks)

50

3 Listen to these people discussing problems at work.

Answer the questions **in English**.

> There is no need to answer these questions in sentences but sometimes an explanation is called for and a one word answer would be inappropriate.

Part 1 Answer questions **3 (a)–3 (c)**.

Example: Where does Aline work? In a hypermarket.

3 (a) What were the young people trying to do and how were they trying to do this?

steal perfume ✓

hiding them under coat ✓

(2 marks)

3 (b) What action did Aline take?

call the boss ✓

(1 mark)

3 (c) What finally happened as the young people were leaving the shop?

police arrived / youths arrested ✓

(1 mark)

Part 2 Answer questions **3 (d)–3 (g)**.

3 (d) What is Marc's job?

fireman ✓

(1 mark)

3 (e) Why had he been called out by the old lady?

cat up tree ✓

cannot get down ✓

(2 marks)

3 (f) What happened to Marc?

He got stuck up tree. ✓

(1 mark)

3 (g) What was his colleagues' reaction?

laughed/found it amusing ✓

(1 mark)

51

4 Michel is talking to his friend, Lola.

Which of the statements are correct?

Write the **five** letters in the boxes.

> Questions with two speakers will require you to focus on every utterance with great care. They can cause some confusion so keep listening!

A	Michel is looking for some shorts.	**B**	Michel thinks the yellow shorts are too expensive.
C	Michel thinks the blue shorts are too short.	**D**	Lola likes the striped skirt best.
E	Lola wants a skirt to wear at a party.	**F**	Michel thinks she should try the skirt on.
G	They both decide to buy an item of clothing.	**H**	Lola ends up buying the red skirt.
I	Lola has forgotten her purse.	**J**	The shop is about to close.

Example: A

4 C ✓

D ✓

E ✓

G ✓

I ✓

in any order

(5 marks)

52

82

5 Listen to Ellie talking about holidays.

For each holiday write a like and dislike.

Write the correct letters in the boxes.

A	clean air
B	luxury
C	weather
D	delays
E	views
F	cost
G	local inhabitants
H	noise
I	food
J	friends
K	activities
L	museums

The options given are structured so that they could be taken as positive or negative in a different context so don't prejudge the responses before you start.

Example:

Holiday	☺	☹
Example: France	A	H

Holiday	☺	☹
5 (a) Spain	G ✓	D ✓
5 (b) Paris	B ✓	I ✓
5 (c) Switzerland	K ✓	C ✓

(6 marks)

---

6 Listen to some people talking about relationships.

Answer the questions.

Write the correct letter in each box.

Many answers will offer plausible alternatives and the vocabulary of several (or none) of the options may be present, so more than ever, focusing on the correct answer will be vital.

Example: What does Romain think of his stepfather?

   A He is generous.   B He is strict.   C He is lazy.

   [B]

Part 1 Listen to Romain talking about relationships.

Answer questions **6 (a)–6 (c)**.

6 **(a)** For how long have Romain's parents been divorced?

   A 8 months   B 10 months   C more than a year

   [C] ✓ *(1 mark)*

6 **(b)** What does Romain say about his mum?

   A She lives close by.   B She lives in Germany.   C He misses her.

   [C] ✓ *(1 mark)*

6 **(c)** Which fact annoys Romain?

   A He cannot find a job.   B His dad does nothing.   C His dad has remarried.

   [B] ✓ *(1 mark)*

Part 2 Listen to Ambre talking about her relationships.

Answer questions **6 (d) and 6 (e)**.

6 **(d)** Why does Ambre not want to go to the party?

   A She will not know anyone there.   B She has nothing suitable to wear.   C Her parents will be there.

   [A] ✓ *(1 mark)*

6 **(e)** Why has she recently split up with her boyfriend?

   A He had started to see another girl.   B He was too possessive.   C He moved to a different town.

   [B] ✓ *(1 mark)*

Part 3 Now listen to Éloïse talking about her family problems.

Answer questions **6 (f) and 6 (g)**.

6 **(f)** What has happened to Éloïse?

   A She had an argument with her mum.   B She argued with her sister.   C She had problems at school.

   [A] ✓ *(1 mark)*

6 **(g)** What does she now regret?

   A making someone cry   B getting angry   C throwing food

   [A] ✓ *(1 mark)*

TOTAL FOR PAPER IS 40 MARKS

1 Read what these three young people say about the environment.

Cécile: Pour moi, la protection de l'environnement est très importante. J'habite dans une grande ville industrielle où la pollution est un problème grave parce qu'il y a plein d'usines qui rejettent de la fumée dans l'air. J'ai écrit au commissaire européen à l'Environnement mais je n'ai pas eu de réponse. C'est scandaleux! Je fais ce que je peux pour aider et je recycle le verre et les journaux.

Marianne: Moi, la protection de l'environnement, ça ne m'intéresse pas vraiment et à mon avis, c'est la responsabilité de notre gouvernement. Je ne recycle rien, cependant, j'utilise souvent les transports en commun au lieu de me déplacer en voiture. Le mois dernier, j'ai persuadé mon père d'acheter une nouvelle voiture hybride. Selon moi, rien ne changera vraiment à l'avenir car beaucoup de gens sont comme moi.

Élodie: Je suis triste quand je vois des gens jeter des papiers dans la rue, même quand il y a une poubelle tout près. De plus, je pense qu'il est important d'essayer de protéger les espèces en voie de disparition, alors j'ai adopté un tigre et je vais m'inscrire dans une association qui lutte contre la cruauté envers les animaux.

Who expresses the following ideas?

Write **C** (Cécile), **M** (Marianne) or **E** (Élodie).

Example: I'm not interested in the environment. **M**

1 (a) I get upset by seeing litter. E ✓ *(1 mark)*

1 (b) Many others share my views. M ✓ *(1 mark)*

1 (c) I'm concerned about factories. C ✓ *(1 mark)*

1 (d) I recycle glass. C ✓ *(1 mark)*

1 (e) I'm going to join a society. E ✓ *(1 mark)*

1 (f) I have made a written complaint. C ✓ *(1 mark)*

1 (g) I think the authorities should take action. M ✓ *(1 mark)*

> Sometimes key words in the question and the passage can provide the correct answer but sometimes you may need to find a word which means the same rather than the exact word you are looking for.

55

2 Read Mohammed's email about his school.

> **Mail**
> Fichier Edition Affichage Composer Envoyer Aide
>
> Mon collège ici en France est super car nos profs nous ont encouragés à établir des liens avec des collèges à l'étranger. Nous avons trouvé un collège partenaire en Tunisie et nous avons pu aider cet établissement en lui envoyant les livres et les ordinateurs dont il avait besoin. Cependant, à mon avis, nous devrions essayer de faire autre chose pour aider les élèves tunisiens. Par exemple, nous pourrions leur offrir de l'aide financière.
> L'année dernière, un groupe d'élèves de notre collège a fait un échange scolaire avec un collège gallois mais malheureusement, je n'y suis pas allé. Mes copains ont remarqué plein de différences entre les deux collèges. Ils ont dit que là-bas, il y a plus de retenues, mais aussi moins de devoirs. Moi, je voudrais bien y aller l'année prochaine car je pense que ça sera vraiment fascinant de goûter à la vie scolaire dans un autre pays.
> Bien que j'aime mon collège, je trouve les bâtiments trop vieux et je crois qu'on pourrait améliorer les installations dans la salle de sport.

Which **five** statements are true?

Write the correct letters in each box.

A	Mohammed likes his school.	B	His school is hoping to be twinned with a school in Tunisia.
C	Mohammed's school has sent IT equipment to another school.	D	His school has an exchange with an English school.
E	Mohammed thinks his school could do more to help pupils in Tunisia.	F	Mohammed has been on a school exchange.
G	The French pupils get more homework than those in the exchange school.	H	Mohammed's school gives more detentions than the exchange school.
I	Mohammed would like to see what life in a school abroad is like.	J	Mohammed thinks his school's buildings are up-to-date.
K	He would like to see better sports facilities.		

Example: A

> You will need to sift out irrelevant or contradictory statements in the text but persevere, you will succeed in the end!

2 C ✓

E ✓

G ✓

I ✓

K ✓ *(5 marks)*

in any order

56

3 Read Antoine's account of a shopping trip.

> La semaine dernière, je suis allé en ville et j'ai fait les magasins tout seul. J'avais décidé d'acheter des cadeaux pour mon frère qui va bientôt avoir seize ans, et pour ma mère qui va célébrer son anniversaire la semaine prochaine. Mon père m'a emmené au centre-ville en voiture avant d'aller à son bureau et j'ai cherché en vain le roman que mon frère veut lire. J'ai réussi à trouver un maillot de foot de son équipe préférée et je l'ai acheté à un prix raisonnable.
>
> Après avoir pris un déjeuner rapide dans un café, je suis entré dans une bijouterie où j'ai passé une demi-heure à chercher une bague en argent pour ma mère, mais sans succès. Vers trois heures de l'après-midi, je passais devant un magasin de vêtements quand j'ai remarqué une belle écharpe en soie et j'ai téléphoné à ma sœur pour lui demander son opinion. Elle m'a dit de l'acheter, alors j'étais vraiment ravi d'avoir trouvé deux cadeaux pour ma famille!

Answer the following questions.

> You will need to sift out irrelevant or contradictory statements in the text but persevere, you will succeed in the end!

Write the correct letter in each box.

Example: The shopping trip took place …

  A last month **B** yesterday **C** last week   **C**

3 (a) Antoine went into town to buy …

  A presents for members of his family **B** something for his father **C** a treat for himself   A ✓ *(1 mark)*

3 (b) His brother is currently …

  A 16 **B** 15 **C** 17   B ✓ *(1 mark)*

3 (c) He went into town …

  A on foot **B** by bus **C** by car   C ✓ *(1 mark)*

3 (d) For his brother Antoine bought …

  A a novel **B** a football shirt **C** a football   B ✓ *(1 mark)*

3 (e) Antoine spent 30 minutes …

  A having lunch **B** in a clothes' shop **C** in a jeweller's shop   C ✓ *(1 mark)*

3 (f) For his mother Antoine bought …

  A a scarf **B** a purse **C** some perfume   A ✓ *(1 mark)*

57

4 Read these comments about healthy lifestyles.

Fill in the gaps using a word from the box.

Write the correct letter.

A	éviter	B	ferons
C	jamais	D	sport
E	eau	F	légumes
G	renoncer	H	arrêter
I	allons	J	viens
K	vais	L	vient
M	trop	N	risquent
O	cancer		

Example: À mon avis, il faut faire du **D** afin de garder la forme.

4 (a) Pour être en meilleure forme, il vaudrait mieux A le fastfood. ✓ *(1 mark)*

4 (b) Mon copain L de commencer à aller au centre sportif deux fois par semaine. ✓ *(1 mark)*

4 (c) Ma mère mangeait M de frites mais maintenant, elle en mange rarement. ✓ *(1 mark)*

4 (d) Mon frère et moi I faire du jogging ensemble à l'avenir. ✓ *(1 mark)*

4 (e) Je vais essayer de boire plus d' E car c'est bon pour la peau. ✓ *(1 mark)*

4 (f) Je fumais dix cigarettes par jour mais j'ai réussi à G au tabac. ✓ *(1 mark)*

4 (g) Je ne prendrai C de drogues. ✓ *(1 mark)*

4 (h) Ceux qui boivent beaucoup d'alcool N d'endommager leur santé. ✓ *(1 mark)*

> You need to be on the ball as regards grammar here. For example, ask yourself what type of word usually comes after à; the normal response would be an infinitive.

58

84

5   Read Arthur's blog about the Internet.

> Je trouve qu'en général, Internet est super mais il y a des choses qui m'inquiètent. Voici ce que j'en pense!
>
> Je pense qu'Internet est indispensable quand on doit faire des recherches scolaires. Je peux tout trouver sans perdre de temps. Il est vrai qu'on peut faire des achats sur Internet sans quitter la maison et que beaucoup d'articles coûtent plus cher dans les magasins. Pourtant, j'aime bien pouvoir essayer des vêtements avant de les acheter.
>
> Ce qui me plaît vraiment, c'est que je peux bavarder avec mes amis et avec mon frère qui habite au Cameroun depuis deux ans sans utiliser mon téléphone. Par contre, je pense qu'il faut faire attention quand on parle à des inconnus sur un forum car il ne faut pas leur donner nos renseignements personnels, c'est nul.

What does Arthur feel about the following?

For each one write **P** (positive), **N** (negative) or **P/N** (positive and negative) in each box.

Example: the Internet   `P/N`

5   (a)   using the Internet for schoolwork   `P`   ✓   *(1 mark)*

5   (b)   shopping online   `P/N`   ✓   *(1 mark)*

5   (c)   staying in touch with people online   `P`   ✓   *(1 mark)*

5   (d)   using chatrooms   `N`   ✓   *(1 mark)*

> Try to make a list of all the ways in which you could work out positive and negative opinions before you attempt such a question and remember that if you see both it will be P/N.

6   Read the following headlines from the media.

A	Tensions rise in East Africa
B	Televised debate on green issues
C	Funding problems hit schools
D	Increase in crime
E	Celebrities to marry
F	Weather problems
G	Fire wrecks building
H	Deforestation a major problem

> In questions like this, a key word can lead you to the answer but be careful, there may be distracters too!

Which headline goes with each description?

Write the correct letter in each box.

Example: Les chefs d'État des pays européens vont discuter des problèmes environnementaux à la télé ce soir.   `B`

6   (a)   Des vents épouvantables ont causé des dégâts sérieux au Sénégal.   `F`   ✓   *(1 mark)*

6   (b)   Un incendie a détruit un bâtiment au centre de Nice.   `G`   ✓   *(1 mark)*

6   (c)   Le chanteur DJ Rapide va épouser la vedette Léa en été.   `E`   ✓   *(1 mark)*

6   (d)   Le taux de criminalité continue à augmenter.   `D`   ✓   *(1 mark)*

7   Read Alice's account of her part-time job.

> Le mois dernier, j'ai trouvé un petit job dans la ville où j'habite. J'ai besoin d'argent supplémentaire car je vais payer mes frais universitaires pour l'année prochaine, donc j'étais vraiment heureuse de voir une petite annonce à l'hôtel de ville. On cherchait quelqu'un pour travailler dans une agence de voyage et, après un entretien, on m'a offert le poste.
>
> Après deux jours de formation, j'étais prête à commencer. J'ai tout de suite aimé mon travail car le contact avec le public me plaît énormément, et comme j'ai déjà fait plein de voyages à l'étranger, j'ai pu aider les gens à choisir leur destination de vacances. Avant-hier une vieille dame est entrée dans l'agence et m'a demandé d'organiser les vacances de ses rêves. Elle était très heureuse quand nous avons réussi à trouver une croisière de luxe aux Caraïbes!

Answer the questions **in English**.

> Make sure that if there are two marks available for a question, you give two details but if there is only one, don't write too much as an inaccuracy could lose you the mark you have already gained from the right answer.

Example: When did Alice get her part-time job?   Last month.

7   (a)   Why did Alice need extra money?

   to pay for university fees   ✓

   (1 mark)

7   (b)   Where did she see the advert for the job?

   in the town hall   ✓

   (1 mark)

7   (c)   What took two days?

   her training   ✓

   (1 mark)

7   (d)   What **two** things did Alice think would make her a suitable candidate for the job?

   She is good with people ✓ and has travelled a lot so could

   offer help with holiday destinations. ✓

   (2 marks)

7   (e)   Why do you think the old lady was happy?

   She was going on her dream holiday. ✓

   (1 mark)

   TOTAL FOR PAPER IS 40 MARKS

1   Listen to these people discussing acts at a talent show.

For each act, write the letter of the act and the speaker's opinion of the act.

For each opinion, write **P** (positive), **N** (negative) or **P/N** (positive and negative) in each box.

A		**B**	
C		**D**	
E		**F**	
G		**H**	
I		**J**	

Letter of act		Opinion		Letter of act		Opinion	
Example:	F	N					
1 (a)	B ✓	P ✓		1 (c)	H ✓	P/N ✓	
1 (b)	J ✓	P ✓		1 (d)	D ✓	N ✓	

(8 marks)

> Where you are asked for two distinct answers it will be important to be ready to hear both from the start. Remember that the French often have two words for the two different genders of a job.

2   Listen to this extract from a reality TV show about house renovations.

A	the living room
B	the garden
C	the loft
D	the downstairs toilet
E	the upstairs toilet
F	the dining room
G	the master bedroom
H	the shower room
I	the guest bedroom
J	the bathroom
K	the entrance hall
L	the kitchen

> Listen for negatives that are intended to distract you from the correct answers. The answers can always be in any order when set out like this.

Which **two** areas of these homes have been renovated?

Write the correct letters in the boxes.

Example: D   F

2   (a)   A ✓   I ✓

2   (b)   J ✓   H ✓

2   (c)   B ✓   C ✓

2   (d)   G ✓   L ✓

(8 marks)

3   Listen to these young French people, Marc, Loïc and Sandrine talking about holidays.

Who would say each of the following?

Write **M** (Marc), **L** (Loïc) or **S** (Sandrine) in the correct boxes.

> It might be useful to make notes as you hear the three sections to help you make your final answers here.

Example: I went on holiday with my aunt.   M

3   (a)   I want to sunbathe.   S ✓   *(1 mark)*

3   (b)   The weather caused a problem on my last holiday.   L ✓   *(1 mark)*

3   (c)   I visit a relative during the holidays.   M ✓   *(1 mark)*

3   (d)   I like water sports.   S ✓   *(1 mark)*

3   (e)   I have been to America recently.   L ✓   *(1 mark)*

3   (f)   My father works abroad.   M ✓   *(1 mark)*

4   Listen to the following extracts.

Where does each one take place?

> Listen for clues which are not the translation of the words in the box as they would be too easy when heard.

Write the correct letter in each box.

A	hotel
B	campsite
C	tourist office
D	chemist's
E	library
F	castle
G	lost property office
H	supermarket
I	museum
J	police station

Example: D

4   (a)   C ✓   *(1 mark)*

4   (b)   G ✓   *(1 mark)*

4   (c)   A ✓   *(1 mark)*

4   (d)   J ✓   *(1 mark)*

5   Listen to Alex talking about his job.

Answer the questions **in English**.

Example: In which city does Alex work?   Marseille

Part 1   Answer questions **5 (a)–5 (c).**

5   **(a)**   For how long has Alex worked for the organisation?

nearly a year ✓

(1 mark)

5   **(b)**   Whom does the charity help?

homeless ✓

(1 mark)

5   **(c)**   From what Alex says, what makes you think that the charity is not large?

only 12 employees ✓

(1 mark)

Part 2   Answer questions **5 (d)–5 (g).**

5   **(d)**   How many days off per week does Alex get?

1 ✓

(1 mark)

5   **(e)**   What was he doing yesterday?

giving out blankets ✓

(1 mark)

5   **(f)**   Give **three** details about the woman Alex met.

about 30 ✓

coughing ✓

cold ✓

(3 marks)

5   **(g)**   Why is Alex still concerned about the woman at the end?

soon be back on streets ✓

(1 mark)

6   Listen to Kathy talking to Clément.

Decide which statements about Kathy are true.

Write the **five** correct letters in the boxes.

A	She has no friends except Clément.
B	She has had an argument with her friend Chloé.
C	Her teachers have criticised her.
D	She never uses social network sites.
E	She feels let down by Chloé.
F	She has been accused by Chloé of cheating in an exam.
G	She will be discussing her problems with her mother tomorrow.
H	She is going to complain to her headteacher.
I	Her friend Chloé is sorry for her actions.
J	She has an appointment for tomorrow afternoon.
K	She may leave her school.
L	Chloé thinks she is stupid.

Example: B

6   E ✓

F ✓

H ✓

K ✓

L ✓

in any order

(5 marks)

TOTAL FOR PAPER IS 40 MARKS

There are no questions printed on this page.

There are no questions printed on this page.

There are no questions printed on this page.

There are no questions printed on this page.

There are no questions printed on this page.

There are no questions printed on this page.

Published by Pearson Education Limited, Edinburgh Gate, Harlow, Essex, CM20 2JE.

www.pearsonschoolsandfecolleges.co.uk

Text and original illustrations © Pearson Education Limited 2013
Edited, produced and typeset by Wearset Ltd, Boldon, Tyne and Wear
Illustrated by Wearset Ltd, Boldon, Tyne and Wear
Cover illustration by Miriam Sturdee

First published 2013

17 16 15 14 13
10 9 8 7 6 5 4 3 2 1

British Library Cataloguing in Publication Data
A catalogue record for this book is available from the British Library

ISBN 9781292013725

Printed in Slovakia by Neografica

Acknowledgements
The publisher would like to thank the following for their kind permission to reproduce their photographs:

(Key: b-bottom; c-centre; l-left; r-right; t-top)

Alamy Images: Peter H Noyce 27; **Corbis:** Tetra Images 42; **Getty Images:** PhotoAlto / James Hardy 55t, StockByte / George Doyle 55b, The Image Bank / John Giustina 52; **Pearson Education Ltd:** Gareth Boden 4t, 4b, 9, 20tl, 20cr, 24, 35c, 35b, Jon Barlow 4c, 14, 20cl, Jörg Carstensen 22c, Jules Selmes 13, 25, Ken Wilson-Max 20bl, MindStudio 22t, 22b, Sophie Bluy 55c, Trevor Clifford 35t; **Photolibrary.com:** Hill Street Studios / Nicole Goddard 43; **Photos.com:** arinahabich 26; **Robert Harding World Imagery:** Gavin Hellier 64; **Veer/Corbis:** Sergey Sukhorukov 41

All other images © Pearson Education Limited

Every effort has been made to trace the copyright holders and we apologise in advance for any unintentional omissions. We would be pleased to insert the appropriate acknowledgement in any subsequent edition of this publication.

In the writing of this book, no examiners authored sections relevant to examination papers for which they have responsibility.